E X P L O D

Welcome to *Explodapedia*, the indispensable guide to everything you need to know!

This series is packed with in-depth knowledge you can trust; it gives you the tools you need to understand the science behind the wonders of our world. Our story begins with *The Cell*, the secret at the heart of all life.

'I had no idea cells were so interesting (or funny)!'
Greg Jenner

'Easy to read for anyone curious about what science has and is discovering... Prepare to be amazed!'
Sir Paul Nurse, Nobel Prize winner

'The perfect balance between charm, quirkiness and wonder... for kids and adults alike.'
Siddhartha Mukherjee, Pulitzer Prize winner

'[These books] lead their readers willingly to the wonders of the biological world.'
Professor Richard Fortey

'Both accessible and funny... a clever way to introduce... our understanding of all life today.'
Professor Venki Ramakrishnan, Nobel Prize winner

BM: To Fi, who gave me the first cell I ever had.

AA: To Karen, Connor and Spencer, my favourite
conglomerations of cells on the planet.

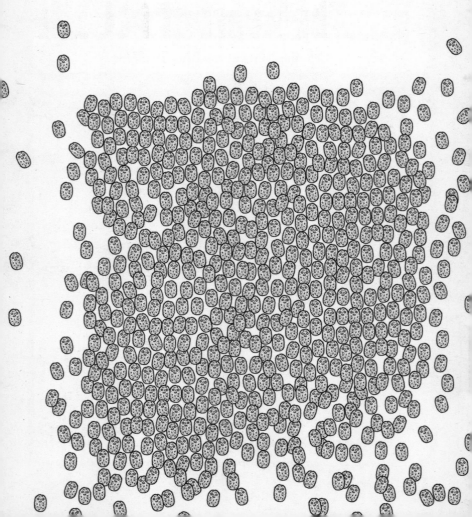

EXPL⊙DAPEDIA
THE CELL
The Heart of ALL Life

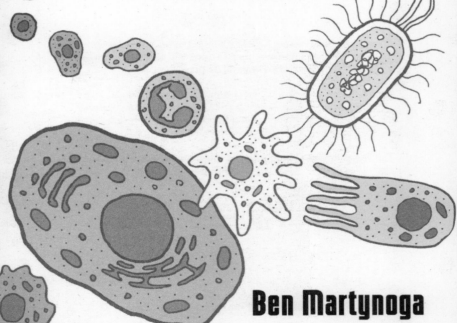

Ben Martynoga

Illustrated by
Moose Allain

David Fickling Books
31 Beaumont Street
Oxford OX1 2NP, UK

Explodapedia: The Cell
is a
DAVID FICKLING BOOK

First published in Great Britain in 2023 by
David Fickling Books,
31 Beaumont Street,
Oxford, OX1 2NP

978-1-78845191-8

1 3 5 7 9 10 8 6 4 2

Papers used by David Fickling Books are from well-managed forests and other
responsible sources.

DAVID FICKLING BOOKS Reg. No. 8340307

A CIP catalogue record for this book is available from the British Library.

Printed and bound in Great Britain by Clays, Ltd, Elcograf S.p.A.

Italic type is used in *Explodapedia* to highlight words that are defined
in the glossary when they first appear, to show quoted material and
the names of published works. Bold type is used for emphasis.

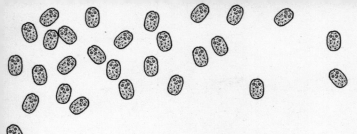

Contents

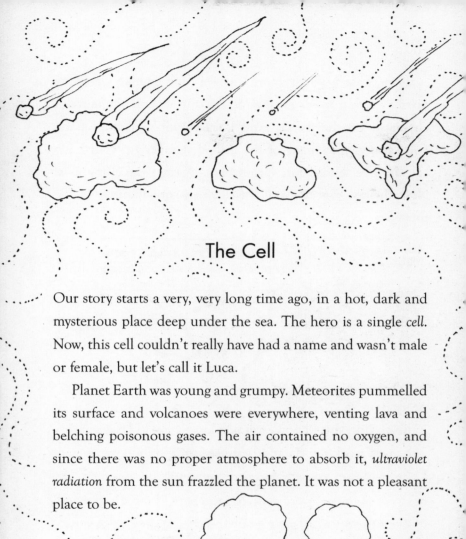

The Cell

Our story starts a very, very long time ago, in a hot, dark and mysterious place deep under the sea. The hero is a single *cell*. Now, this cell couldn't really have had a name and wasn't male or female, but let's call it Luca.

Planet Earth was young and grumpy. Meteorites pummelled its surface and volcanoes were everywhere, venting lava and belching poisonous gases. The air contained no oxygen, and since there was no proper atmosphere to absorb it, *ultraviolet radiation* from the sun frazzled the planet. It was not a pleasant place to be.

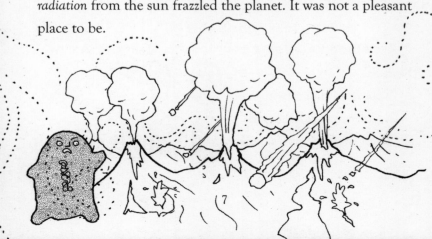

Luca wasn't much more than a tiny bubble of living matter – a thin *membrane* skin on the outside and a mixture of chemicals on the inside. And Luca couldn't do any of the fancy things that many of the cells that make up your body can do, like sense light, sprout hairs or carry *nerve* impulses. Nevertheless, this tiny cell was hellbent on dominating the universe.

But do you know what? Luca's world-conquering plan was working. That's because, four billion years ago, Luca managed to *self-reproduce*. Self-reproduction basically means making a copy of yourself, and here's how it happened.

First the little cell grew a bit, and then it divided into two. Simple.

Now Luca had a twin.

Each twin divided again.

Then there were four cells.

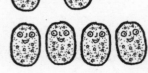

Those cells doubled again to make eight. And again (16). And again (32), and again, and again.

After this had happened 10 times, over 1,000 Lucas had been born.

After just 60 of these divisions, things were getting a bit out of hand: as many as 1,152,921,504,606,847,000*Lucas had entered the world.

*That's more than a quintillion (one million trillion) cells – an almost unimaginably huge number. It's 1,000 times more than the (estimated) number of ants in the whole world today.

Luca was special because it was the first cell that truly mastered the ability to *reproduce* by dividing one cell into two. And, thinking about it, for one cell to build another new and more or less identical cell completely from scratch is pretty amazing. But that's self-reproduction for you. And if it sounds like quite a straightforward thing to do, it most definitely isn't.

This kind of self-reproduction was the little cell's superpower.

I'm Luca.

No, I'm Luca!

Luca was lucky enough to carry a sort of personal instruction manual around on its insides, written in a chemical language called *DNA* (more on this later). The DNA contained detailed plans for building the cell, keeping it alive, dividing it in two and, crucially, making sure that each new cell carried exactly the same plans for making more Lucas. Without DNA, cells would never have been able to reproduce themselves.

It was lucky, too, that Luca had found the perfect spot to hang out: a *hydrothermal vent* - that's a crack in the seabed where hot mineral-rich water and gas pour out of the Earth's crust and mingle with the seawater. Luca sucked up a never-ending stream of hot chemicals from the vent and used them to make all the energy a little cell could possibly need to keep on growing and dividing.

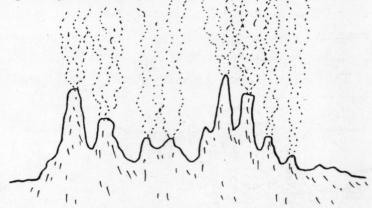

With a reliable source of energy and the ability to self-reproduce, a world of opportunities opened up for Luca.

Next stop, global domination . . .

Your Least Famous but Most Important Ancestor

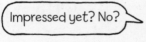

Impressed yet? No?

Well, what if you found out that Luca is part of your family? Your direct ancestor, in fact. Which basically means: no Luca, no you.

And look out of the window. See all those living things? They might look different, but they actually all have a huge amount in common.

Rotting apple

They're all either cells or made from cells. In fact, all living things on this planet are based on cells. No cells, no life.

Most cells are so tiny that they're completely invisible without a powerful microscope. But we know they're there.

What you think of as 'you' is made from several trillion human cells. A cat – because it is smaller than you – is made from rather fewer cat cells, all working together to make a cat. And that great big apple tree is made from rather more apple tree cells. That festering apple, meanwhile, is a riot of cellular activity:

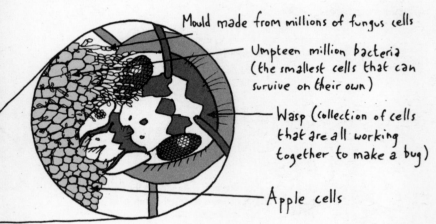

Mould made from millions of fungus cells

Umpteen million bacteria (the smallest cells that can survive on their own)

Wasp (collection of cells that are all working together to make a bug)

Apple cells

And, believe it or not, every single one of those cells is Luca's direct descendant. You see, Luca wasn't the very first cell, or even the very first living thing on the planet. But it was the first cell that divided and whose *offspring* survived and thrived.

What that means is that every single creature alive today is related to Luca*, so they are all related to each other. And to you. No Luca, no life.

*Luca's name actually stands for Last Universal Common Ancestor.

A Planet of Cells

All those cells that Luca started producing four billion years ago have just kept on dividing and multiplying ever since. For year after year, millennium after millennium, they've gone on producing more and more cells.

Today, cells live on and in every nook and cranny of our planet's surface:

Moss and *lichen* cells cling to a mountain's highest peaks

Bacteria cells survive for hundreds of years inside insanely cold icebergs

Ants exist in the driest deserts, even at scorching temperatures of up to 70° C

Scientists have even discovered cells floating in the air several kilometres up in the atmosphere, as well as more than a kilometre below ground inside hot, dark crushing rocks. And, as far as we know, they're all living very contented lives.

In short, cells are everywhere, and they're all related. Every single cell that's alive today is connected to the same gigantic family tree. And Luca is the tiny seed that this entire family has grown from.

The little family of cells that Luca started to raise four billion years ago has coped with any number of volcanic eruptions, earthquakes, tsunamis and meteorite strikes. Not to mention the constant attacks of deadly *viruses*, famines and all manner of other battles for survival. Along the way, such a vast number of Luca's family members have died that scientists couldn't even begin to count them. And billions more cells die every second. But somehow, against all the odds, Luca's family clung on and flourished. Luca's family is your family. It's our family. We call this family 'life', and we are all in it together.

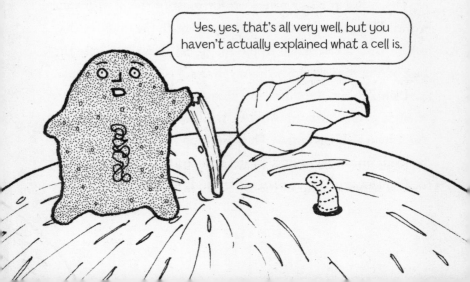

Yes, yes, that's all very well, but you haven't actually explained what a cell is.

CHAPTER 1
What is a Cell?
SURVIVAL MACHINES

Dump a rock in your garden, and it will sit there for years, doing very little indeed. Build a snowman, and before too long it will melt into a muddy puddle (unless you live near the South Pole!).

That's just the way things go for most of the stuff in our world. Things tend to either stay pretty much the same, or they get broken, decay or fall to pieces. Which is why, despite the best of intentions, your bedroom always gets messier with time.

Living things are different. They are full of activity, always changing and constantly working hard to maintain themselves. And living things grow. They multiply. In fact, life seems hellbent on surviving and creating more life.

Plant an apple pip in your garden and, all being well, the little seed will sprout in the spring. Eventually, that brave green shoot turns into a young tree. The sapling grows. More branches appear, more leaves, a thicker trunk and ever deeper roots.

And it's not only the tree that flourishes. Over time, lichens and mosses spread across its bark. Worms, beetles, woodlice and other little critters take up residence beneath the soil, and slender strands of *fungus* wrap tightly round the tree's roots. Bacteria and viruses drift in on the breeze and try their luck at infecting the tree. A blackbird decides that the highest branch makes a convenient singing perch. The cat decides this is a rich hunting ground.

Eventually, the new tree bears fruit. And in the core of each shiny red apple are five or six little pips, each of which carries the potential to grow into an entire new tree. The whole process can start again.

Life is brilliant at making more life.

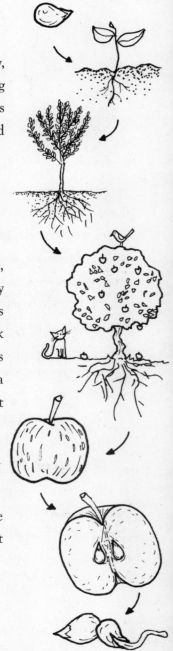

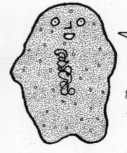

Well, that's hardly news after four billion years!

True, but we mustn't ever take it for granted. The life forms here on Earth are truly, utterly unique.

Think about it: the universe is unbelievably massive, but this is the only part of it where we know for certain that life exists. That means there could be more life blooming under the nail of your little finger than there is in the rest of the cosmos.

All objects are made from the same stuff – chemical *atoms* and *molecules* – and they all obey the same physical laws, like gravity. So why are living things so completely different from the boring rock, the melting snowman and your untidy bedroom?

An important clue to unravelling that mystery is the fact that life is made from cells.

This is actually the single most important thing to know about cells – and the key to understanding what they are. The cell is the basic unit of life. It's the smallest thing that has all the features necessary for it to be considered alive. Everything that is alive is either a cell or a collection of cells.

Single cell

Collection of cells

A cell is like a miniature machine, built entirely from

chemicals and fuelled by chemicals. Each of these cell machines aims to build itself up, maintain itself and keep itself running for as long as it possibly can. To do that it has to start up a huge number of different chemical reactions and then do all it can to keep them going, come what may.

Think of a juggler in a circus – if she drops her flaming clubs, the crowd boos and her act is basically over. If a cell fails to keep its chemical reactions going, it's not just the show that ends, the cell itself dies.

Because of this need to keep going, each and every cell is a restless, fizzing little bubble of life, whose only ambition is to survive and reproduce. All cells that are alive today inherited this ambition from Luca, their most ancient ancestor.

Yup, it's thanks to me that even the tiniest cells in the biggest bodies are very much alive!

When you consider the fact that many – perhaps even most – cells spend their entire existence as single cells, the idea that they are all independent living things might seem kind of obvious. That's how most bacteria live. There are billions of different kinds of them, and they turn up absolutely everywhere (at this very moment there are trillions of them living inside your guts, up your nose, under your armpits and pretty much everywhere else on and in your body). And bacteria cells are most definitely alive.

Think of all the cells that make up the bodies of plants and animals. They're all living individuals too. If you cut some of those cells off from the main body that grew them, they don't just curl up and die. Not immediately, at least.

When you bite into an apple, you're actually chomping up millions of still living apple cells!

Don't eat us!

Cells of all fresh fruit and veg are 100% alive, until they droop and rot.

Noooo!

Murderers!

It's even true of our bodies. Accidentally chop off the tip of your finger with a sharp knife (ouch!) and those fingertip cells can't last long, can they? Surely they'd need your heart and lungs to keep them going?

Well, if you could get your severed fingertip over to a well-equipped research lab – and if you asked the resident biologists nicely – they could probably pop your finger cells into a warm incubator, bubble them with oxygen and feed them a soup of nutrients. Then they could keep your cells alive for weeks.

So, all cells are most definitely alive. The next thing we need to know is that they come in a huge variety of shapes and sizes.

MASSIVE CELLS AND MIDGET CELLS

Most cells are so tiny we can't see them without a microscope (or maybe a magnifying glass). But there are a few exceptions.

If you ate an egg for breakfast this morning, consider this: that egg yolk was just one single, gigantic cell. All birds' eggs are the same. Once an ostrich egg is *fertilized*, the baby ostrich starts to develop from a cell that's about the size of a tennis ball and not at all hard to see.

Other cells are both massive and microscopically invisible:

• Some nerve cells in your body stretch all the way from the base of your spine to the tips of your toes.

• Biologists think that some nerve cells in the bodies of blue whales extend from the skin of their tails into their brains – that's up to 30 metres!

Human nerve cell: 1m long
Blue whale nerve cell: 30 m long

Hang on, how can whale nerve cells be huge *and* invisible?

Yup, that might seem a bit confusing. The thing is, although these cells can be very long indeed, they're also unbelievably skinny – just a few thousandths of a millimetre wide! Our eyes simply cannot see anything as thin as they are.

The majority of cells are microscopic in every dimension. To get an idea of how small most cells are, hold your sleeve up to the light. The tiny fibres that stick up and catch the light are some of the thinnest things your eyes can see. They're about 25 microns* wide – line 40 of them up side by side and they'd only fill up one millimetre on a ruler. Even so, they're much wider than most living cells.

*A micron is a millionth of a metre.

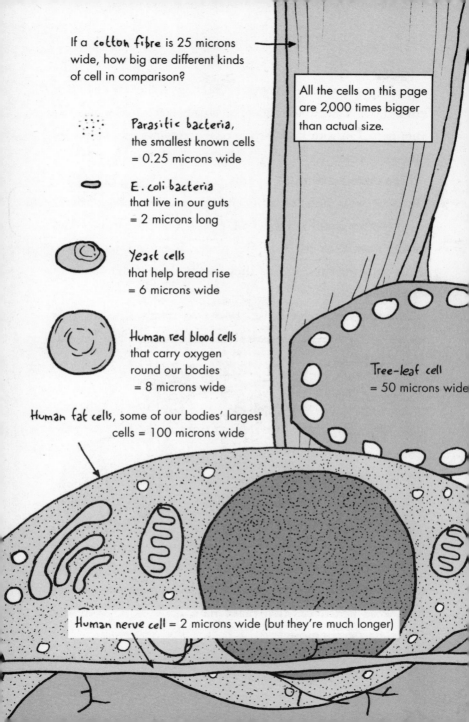

If a **cotton fibre** is 25 microns wide, how big are different kinds of cell in comparison?

All the cells on this page are 2,000 times bigger than actual size.

Parasitic bacteria,
the smallest known cells
= 0.25 microns wide

E. coli bacteria
that live in our guts
= 2 microns long

Yeast cells
that help bread rise
= 6 microns wide

Human red blood cells
that carry oxygen
round our bodies
= 8 microns wide

Tree-leaf cell
= 50 microns wide

Human fat cells, some of our bodies' largest
cells = 100 microns wide

Human nerve cell = 2 microns wide (but they're much longer)

Living LEGO

From the tiny blob-like cells of parasitic bacteria to the insanely long nerves in your body, living cells come in a huge range of different forms.

You can actually think of cells as a kind of living LEGO set. Given enough time and a big enough box of bricks, a LEGO maestro can build a model of pretty much anything. And having a wide variety of LEGO pieces, like windows, wheels, wings and winches, means they can build a wider range of structures.

It's the same with cells. Having so many different cells means living things can take shape in all sorts of weird and wonderful ways.

Fly-eating pitcher plants

Glow-in-the-dark mushrooms

Armadillo

And our bodies are built from muscle cells that can contract, white blood cells that can crawl and gobble up germs, eye cells that sense light, cells that make hair, nails, skin, teeth and bones, and many more.

The Three Main Kinds of Living Thing

All living things are made from one of three types of cell. These cells are going to crop up quite often in the rest of the book, so let's take a moment to get familiar with them:

Bacteria – say *back-teary-a*. These single cells are generally small and simple. That hasn't held them back, though; there are more bacteria cells on the planet than any other type of cell.

Archaea – say *are-kay-a*. These cells look quite similar to bacteria, but some of the chemical reactions that happen inside *archaea* are very different. They often live in unlikely places, such as boiling-hot salty water, or buried in mud, where there's basically no air at all.

Eukaryotes – say *you-carry-oats*. You're made from *eukaryote* cells and so are all animals, plants and fungi. Eukaryote cells are usually more complicated than those of other living things. We'll find out how they first formed in Chapter 7, and in the next chapter we'll even venture inside one.

Biologists call living things made from these different kinds of cell the three 'domains of life'.

There's an eye-popping variety of living cells out there, but when scientists ask how all these different cells actually work – whether they're bacteria, archaea or eukaryotes – they come to a surprising conclusion. These cells aren't just related; they're all made from the same basic parts and work in more or less the same way.

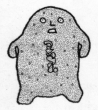

You're really comparing little me to the 30-metre-long nerve cell of a blue whale?!

Absolutely right. Even though cells can look very different on the surface, their most essential chemical processes – the ones that keep them alive and allow them to grow and reproduce themselves – are all amazingly similar. However hard you search, you'll never find a cell without a membrane, or one whose *genes* aren't made from DNA, for example.

The best way for us to see what these different processes are, and find out how cells are organized, is to do the impossible: take a tour around the inside of a living cell.

So, hop aboard and let's venture into Cell City.

CELL CITY – THIS WAY

DRONE TOURS

CHAPTER 2
Welcome to Cell City

Buckle up! The trip to Cell City starts in a few minutes.

We're about to visit a human cell that's been blown up until it's about a kilometre wide and a kilometre high. We can't take a bus tour, instead, we'll find ourselves suspended in a jelly-like gloop, as we fly in a specially modified drone that can travel in any direction we choose.

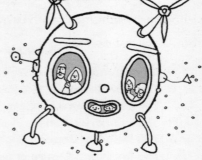

Before we take off, there's some information you need to check out.

▢◯HUMAN CELL CITY TOUR

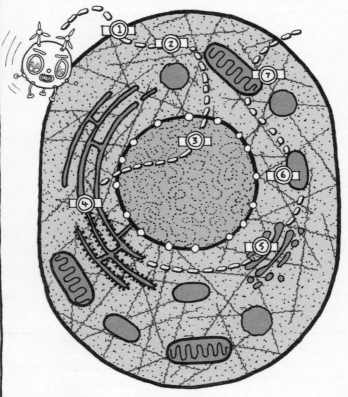

- ▢①▢ **City Boundary** or Cell Membrane
- ▢②▢ **The City Streets** or *Cytoplasm*
- ▢③▢ **The Data Centre** or *Nucleus*
- ▢④▢ **The Industrial Zone** or *Endoplasmic Reticulum* (ER)
- ▢⑤▢ **The Delivery Depot** or *Golgi Apparatus*
- ▢⑥▢ **The Recycling Centre** or *Lysosomes, Peroxisomes* and *Proteasomes*
- ▢⑦▢ **The Power Stations** or *Mitochondria*

The Basics

A lot has to happen to keep a city running. It needs a transport network to shift things around, waste-disposal systems to keep it tidy, power stations to make energy, factories to make stuff, warehouses to store things and some kind of local government to take decisions. A cell is just the same.

When you first enter Cell City, it might look like mayhem, but this is actually a really, really well-organized place. On the map you can see some of the purpose-built structures where many of the crucial processes that keep the cell going happen. The biggest are called *organelles* and they make up the main landmarks, buildings and *infrastructure* that we're going to see in Cell City.

Brace yourselves. It's time to set off on the trip of a lifetime!

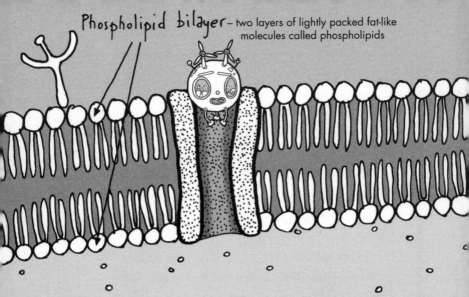

Phospholipid bilayer – two layers of lightly packed fat-like molecules called phospholipids

① ENTERING THE CITY: THE CELL MEMBRANE

We can see into the cell now as we wait to get inside. Cell City is protected by a huge transparent bubble – it looks a bit like a snow globe. What seems like the glass of the snow globe is the cell's membrane and it isn't glass-like at all – it's actually made up of oily substances called *lipids*, which make it a kind of fluid.

The world outside the cell is a dangerous one, so the membrane has to be very careful about which substances it lets into the cell. Because its lipid walls are so flexible, and its *protein pores* can open and shut like gateways, the membrane makes sure helpful substances can get in, but it's also strong enough and strict enough to keep most harmful substances out.

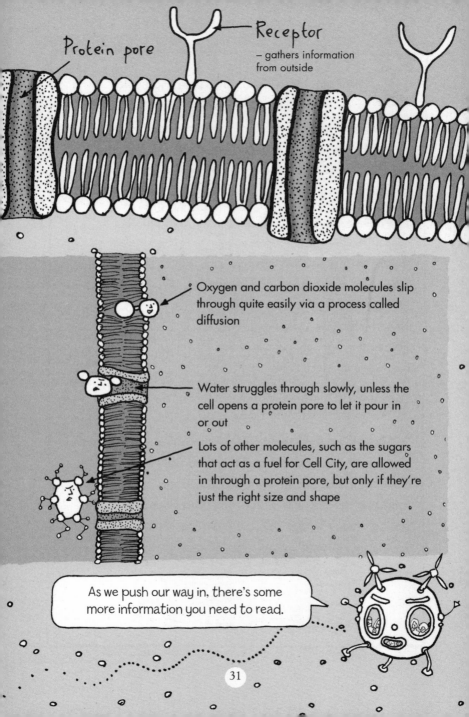

Protein pore

Receptor
– gathers information from outside

Oxygen and carbon dioxide molecules slip through quite easily via a process called diffusion

Water struggles through slowly, unless the cell opens a protein pore to let it pour in or out

Lots of other molecules, such as the sugars that act as a fuel for Cell City, are allowed in through a protein pore, but only if they're just the right size and shape

As we push our way in, there's some more information you need to read.

The Four Main Kinds of Large Molecule that Build and Run Cell City

If you've ever read the back of a cereal packet, you'll have heard of proteins, fats and *carbohydrates*. *Nucleic acids* are made by combining certain carbohydrates with other, smaller molecules.

1. Proteins Even a small cell usually contains over 40 million protein molecules. They're the hardest workers in Cell City. Some of them form the cell's more solid structures, while lots of the others – the ones called *enzymes* – trigger the chemical reactions that keep cells alive. Enzymes can make, break, change or join together different kinds of molecule.

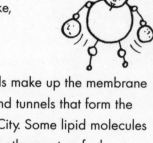

2. Lipids (including fats) Lipids make up the membrane walls and all the bubbles, tubes and tunnels that form the main organelle 'buildings' in Cell City. Some lipid molecules send and receive information, and others act as fuel, storing energy for the cell to use another time.

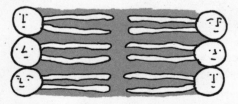

3. Carbohydrates (including starches and sugars)

These molecules provide most of the energy that powers Cell City. They're important raw material for making many of the other kinds of molecule found in cells too. They can also be combined with proteins and lipids and attached to the outside of the cell to help protect it.

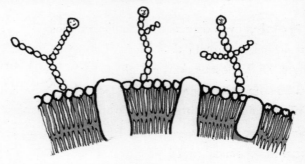

4. Nucleic acids

These are long, string-like molecules that handle the information needed to build and run Cell City. They come in two main types: DNA (deoxyribonucleic acid), which is what genes (see Stop 3) are made from, and *RNA (ribonucleic acid)*, which delivers messages from the DNA genes to the rest of the cell.

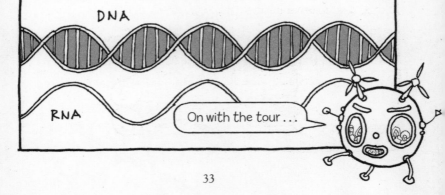

On with the tour . . .

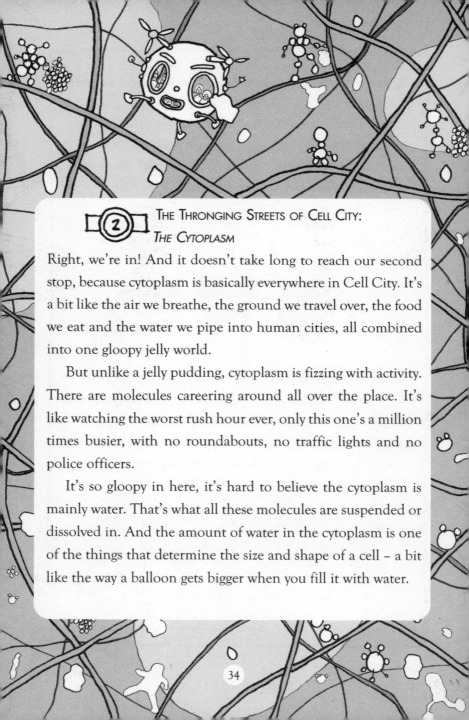

2 THE THRONGING STREETS OF CELL CITY: *THE CYTOPLASM*

Right, we're in! And it doesn't take long to reach our second stop, because cytoplasm is basically everywhere in Cell City. It's a bit like the air we breathe, the ground we travel over, the food we eat and the water we pipe into human cities, all combined into one gloopy jelly world.

But unlike a jelly pudding, cytoplasm is fizzing with activity. There are molecules careering around all over the place. It's like watching the worst rush hour ever, only this one's a million times busier, with no roundabouts, no traffic lights and no police officers.

It's so gloopy in here, it's hard to believe the cytoplasm is mainly water. That's what all these molecules are suspended or dissolved in. And the amount of water in the cytoplasm is one of the things that determine the size and shape of a cell – a bit like the way a balloon gets bigger when you fill it with water.

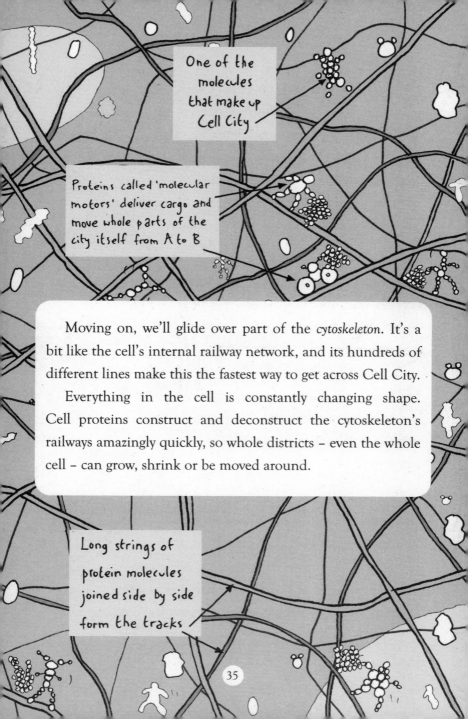

One of the molecules that make up Cell City

Proteins called 'molecular motors' deliver cargo and move whole parts of the city itself from A to B

Moving on, we'll glide over part of the *cytoskeleton*. It's a bit like the cell's internal railway network, and its hundreds of different lines make this the fastest way to get across Cell City.

Everything in the cell is constantly changing shape. Cell proteins construct and deconstruct the cytoskeleton's railways amazingly quickly, so whole districts – even the whole cell – can grow, shrink or be moved around.

Long strings of protein molecules joined side by side form the tracks

We're about to plunge smack bang into the nucleus – the very heart of Cell City. It's home to the 'super-computers' that run the city like a local government, so security is tight. To get in we'll be squeezing through another protein gateway, called a *nuclear pore*.

NUCLEUS

Nuclear pore

> Looks like we're landing in a bowl of giant spaghetti!

Yes, those wriggly things are the cell's *chromosomes* (extremely long molecules of DNA, with various proteins attached). Human cells have 46 of them altogether. They carry more than 20,000 genes between them – and each gene is like a computer program that holds precise instructions for building and

*At normal cell size they'd be a full two metres long. The DNA thread is incredibly thin.

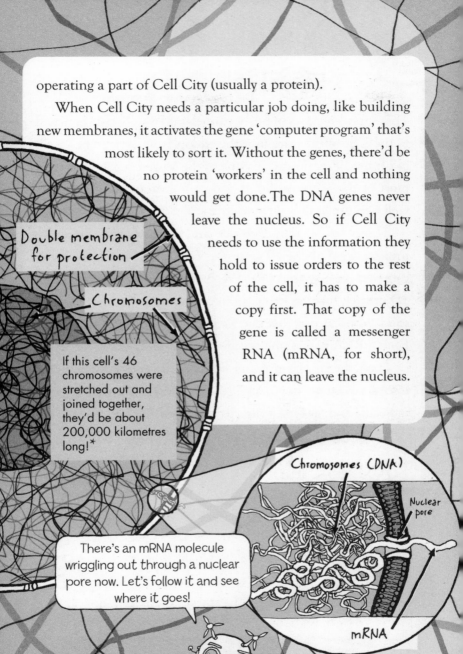

operating a part of Cell City (usually a protein).

When Cell City needs a particular job doing, like building new membranes, it activates the gene 'computer program' that's most likely to sort it. Without the genes, there'd be no protein 'workers' in the cell and nothing would get done. The DNA genes never leave the nucleus. So if Cell City needs to use the information they hold to issue orders to the rest of the cell, it has to make a copy first. That copy of the gene is called a messenger RNA (mRNA, for short), and it can leave the nucleus.

Double membrane for protection

Chromosomes

If this cell's 46 chromosomes were stretched out and joined together, they'd be about 200,000 kilometres long!*

Chromosomes (DNA)

Nuclear pore

mRNA

There's an mRNA molecule wriggling out through a nuclear pore now. Let's follow it and see where it goes!

4 THE INDUSTRIAL ZONE:
THE ENDOPLASMIC RETICULUM

That sprawling mass of tubes, tunnels and warehouses attached to the edge of the nucleus is the endoplasmic reticulum – we'll call it the ER for short. It's one of the biggest organelles. Here most of the proteins, lipids and carbohydrates that make up Cell City are built – on a massive scale.

Those bulky, round things are *ribosomes* and there are thousands of them all over the cell, with crowds of them gathered round parts of the ER. Each ribosome acts a bit like a 3D printer, turning strings of information from the genes into solid, physical proteins that can actually do stuff in the cell. Each mRNA makes one specific kind of protein.

Look, the mRNA molecule we were following is disappearing into a ribosome now! And it's 3D-printing a new protein molecule and feeding it directly into the ER.

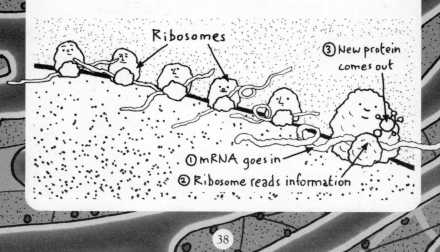

Ribosomes

③ New protein comes out

① mRNA goes in
② Ribosome reads information

The ER is like a hi-tech factory production line, with hundreds of different kinds of enzyme working hard 24/7. They each crack on with one specific job, then pass their work along the line as they gradually build all sorts of fancy proteins, lipids and carbohydrates that the cell needs.

Enzyme production line

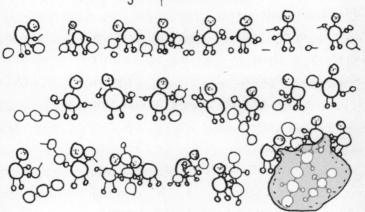

When new products get to the end of the ER assembly line, they don't travel on alone. It's like a whole room full of them detaches itself from the ER factory, jumps onto a cytoskeleton trackway and is shunted over to the Golgi apparatus by molecular motor proteins.

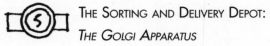

THE SORTING AND DELIVERY DEPOT:
THE GOLGI APPARATUS

Our next stop, the Golgi (gol-jee) apparatus, is like the busiest Amazon online shopping warehouse in the world. Only much busier. Quite a lot of the proteins, lipids and carbohydrates freshly made in the ER will pass straight into here to be finished off, sorted, packed and then delivered wherever they're needed. That might be outside the cell – such as the snot made by the cells that line the inside of your nose.

Once a new bundle arrives from the ER, it becomes part of the packing and delivery depot. Cell membranes are cool like that; they can easily change shape and morph together – like the way bubbles of soap can fuse – to do what Cell City needs them to do.

Membranes fuse, releasing newly made proteins into the Golgi

GOODS IN

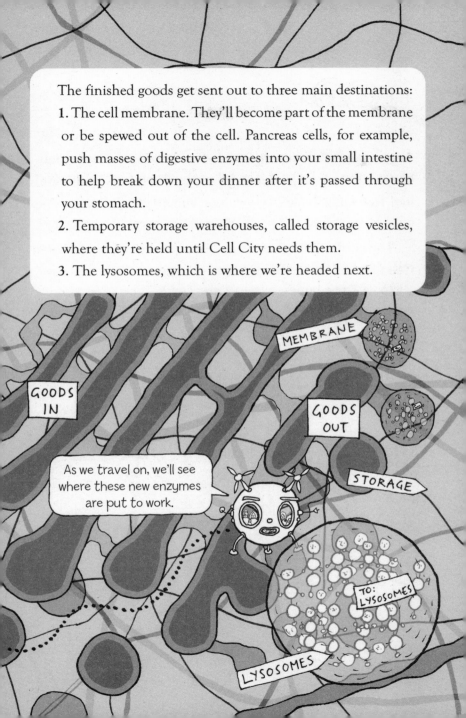

The finished goods get sent out to three main destinations:
1. The cell membrane. They'll become part of the membrane or be spewed out of the cell. Pancreas cells, for example, push masses of digestive enzymes into your small intestine to help break down your dinner after it's passed through your stomach.
2. Temporary storage warehouses, called storage vesicles, where they're held until Cell City needs them.
3. The lysosomes, which is where we're headed next.

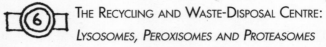

6 THE RECYCLING AND WASTE-DISPOSAL CENTRE:
LYSOSOMES, PEROXISOMES AND PROTEASOMES

Absolutely nothing gets wasted in Cell City. Everything that can be recycled, is recycled, including hazardous waste – and some cell reactions produce a lot of that. There's NO pollution and NO rubbish here. If only our human cities were so well run.

Thousands of small recycling centres are spread throughout Cell City with three different types of depot, which each have a crucial role to play.

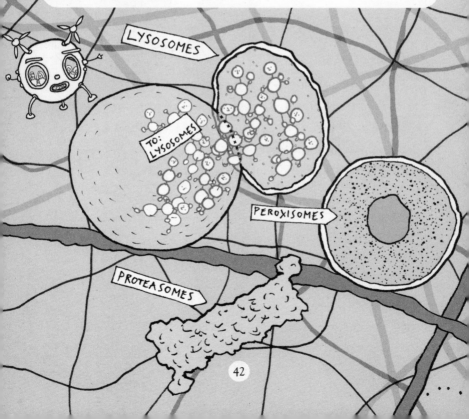

• **Lysosomes** Sloshing with acid and packed full of enzymes, lysosomes are brilliant at snipping up large molecules. Nutrients from the food you eat might get sent here to be  broken down into smaller bits and recycled for use in the cell. And if alien invaders, like viruses, find their way into Cell City, the cell will try to send them straight to the lysosomes to be chomped up and destroyed.

• **Peroxisomes** Greasy, indigestible fat molecules might come here to be broken down for the energy that's locked up inside them. Peroxisomes also make various parts needed to produce new cell membranes.

• **Proteasomes** If there's too much of a particular protein knocking around, or a protein can't do its job because it's the wrong shape, it will go in one end of a proteasome and be spat out the other in hundreds of tiny pieces, which then get reused to build new proteins.

The constant activity in Cell City needs a lot of power to keep it going, but where does it come from? We're about to find out.

(7) THE POWER STATIONS:
MITOCHONDRIA

Cells can each have tens, hundreds or even thousands of mitochondria. And when their need for energy goes up – e.g. if cells in a particular muscle are tensed again and again during exercise training – they'll make even more. Without mitochondria, everything in Cell City would immediately grind to a halt.

The final steps of one of the most important chemical reactions in the known universe happen in the mitochondria. The reaction is called 'cellular respiration', and almost all living cells do it, one way or another, although they don't all need to use oxygen. Here's how it usually goes in most human cells:

Sugar + Oxygen ⟹ Water + Carbon Dioxide + Energy (ATP)

ATP 🔋

The mitochondria capture a lot of the energy released by this reaction and store it in small molecules that act like tiny batteries. The battery molecules are called *adenosine triphosphate* (or *ATP*), and each cell can make tens of millions of them every second! Amazingly, the cells in your body together produce the equivalent of your entire body weight in

ATP every single day (they use it up just as quickly, though, which is why your weight doesn't keep doubling!).

This protein enzyme needs power to get its job done

Energy released

Reinventing the Wheel

Humans invented wheels in around 4000 BCE, for making pottery and carts that trundled around, but living things started using wheels more than three billion years before humans even existed.

An enzyme called ATP synthase is crucial to the mitochondria's ability to capture energy. Working like a turbine in a hydroelectric power station, it makes three ATP molecules every time it spins all the way round. It can rotate as many as 350 times per second, which is much faster than the engine in a Formula One racing car!

Our batteries are running out of charge. It's just as well we've finished the tour.

If you've enjoyed visiting human Cell City, check out these two trips coming your way soon.

◻◯◻ BACTERIA CELL CITY TOUR

It may be about ten times smaller than plant and animal cell cities, and it doesn't have any true organelles, but it's amazingly self-sufficient and a miniature masterpiece of engineering.

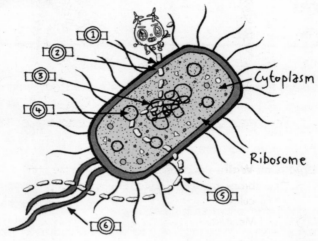

Cytoplasm

Ribosome

◻①◻ Cell wall

◻②◻ **Cell Membrane** – most ATP is made here.

◻③◻ **Chromosome** – not in a nucleus – no bacteria or archaea cells have a nucleus.

◻④◻ **Plasmid DNA** – extra genes on circular pieces of DNA.

◻⑤◻ **Pili** – help bacteria stick to things.

◻⑥◻ **Flagellum** – a massive rotating tail used as a powerful propeller. This city can travel!

⬭◯⬭ PLANT CELL CITY TOUR

It's got lots of the cool stuff we've seen in the human cell and some fantastic highlights that are unique to plant life.

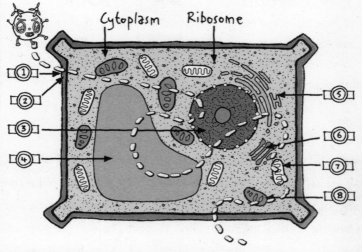

① **Cell Wall** – thick defences built outside the cell membrane, made mainly from huge carbohydrate molecules.

② Cell Membrane

③ Nucleus

④ **Vacuole** – massive reservoir for storing water and other useful substances. When they run low on water, plants wilt.

⑤ ER

⑥ Golgi Apparatus

⑦ Mitochondria

⑧ **Chloroplasts** – bright green organelles that capture sunlight and use it to turn water and carbon dioxide into sugar (food).

CHAPTER 3
Microscopic Marvels
CELLS ARE DISCOVERED – AT LAST

Until 350 years ago, nobody had any idea what a cell was, what one looked like or that their bodies were made up of trillions of cells, all working together. But then along came a particularly inquisitive bunch of cells called Robert Hooke. He gave cells their name and was the first person ever to knowingly see one.

Hooke was incredibly clever as a child and great at inventing and building mechanical contraptions. He once took a brass clock to pieces, then built a working replica from wood. When he grew up, Hooke became an architect, a mathematician, an astronomer, a chemist, and – as if that wasn't enough – a biologist.

He loved to peer down microscopes, which he made himself, to see the tiniest things come into focus. Some of his microscopes

Hooke's microscope

could magnify objects to fifty times their actual size. A pea would look as big as a basketball.

Hooke put all kinds of things – living and dead – under his lenses and recorded what he saw with accurate, stunningly beautiful drawings and detailed notes. In 1665 he published his pictures and descriptions in a book called *Micrographia: or Some Physiological Descriptions of Minute Bodies Made by Magnifying Glasses. With Observations and Inquiries Thereupon.*

The subtitle wasn't exactly catchy, but the book became a bestseller and made Hooke a bit of a celebrity. Among many other things, it showed:

• Hooke's own blood inside the guts of a tiny louse that had bitten him.

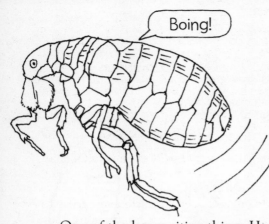

Boing!

• Giant fleas that look like they're about to hop off the page.

• Close-ups of a fly's compound eyes that stare right back at the reader.

One of the less exciting things Hooke showed in the book was a sliver of cork from a wine bottle. Through his powerful lenses he had seen that cork bark was made up of thousands of tiny chambers. They reminded him of the small 'cells' that monks lived in. So that's what he called them.

But the cork cells Hooke looked at weren't really living cells at all. They were the dead and hollowed-out remains of cells (filled with air

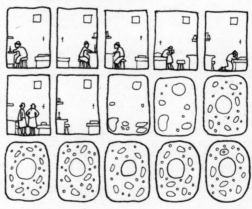

– which is why cork floats so well). Now we also know that, unlike the ones in cork, most cells don't have a regular shape (see p. 21). So 'cell' wasn't the best name Hooke could have chosen, but, amazingly, it stuck.

A few years after publishing his famous book, Hooke was given some mysterious, illustrated letters written by a researcher he'd never heard of. They described tiny living creatures – the author called them 'animalcules' – that were even smaller than Hooke's cork cells.

At first, Hooke was downright sceptical. He even tried to look for these little beasties himself, but couldn't spot them. He suspected his correspondent was making things up. After all, these letters weren't even written in Latin – the language of scientists – they were in Dutch.

As it happened, the sender wasn't a highly trained scientist, he was an unknown fabric merchant called Antonie van Leeuwenhoek.

Leeuwenhoek's microscope

Somehow, this nobody from Holland had come up with a completely new way to make microscopes that had magnification at least five times better than the ones Hooke was so proud of. The cheeky Dutchman could magnify up to 275 times original size – that pea would now be the size of a fat cow – help! And what van Leeuwenhoek lacked in scientific education, he more than made up for with *insatiable* curiosity.

There's no fleas on me, love.

Like Hooke, he put anything and everything he could find under the microscope; he even used his own body as a lab.

• He scraped plaque from his teeth and saw the bacteria that cause tooth decay. This was the first time anyone had seen bacteria!

• In 1673, he cut himself and described his blood as consisting of 'small, round globules'. This is probably the first description of human cells ever.

• He even saw sperm cells swimming around in a drop of his own *semen*.

Race you!

For many people alive at the time, including scientists like Hooke, the most shocking of all van Leeuwenhoek's discoveries was his claim that a single drop of water contained more than eight million tiny alien creatures. He called the smallest ones '*very wee animals*' (probably bacteria) . . .

. . . and the slightly larger ones '*gygantick monsters*' (we now call these single-celled *protists* and *algae*).

Eventually, Hooke managed to build microscopes that were nearly as powerful as van Leeuwenhoek's. And when he looked through them, he realized that the Dutchman's wild claims were absolutely true!

By the start of the 1700s, through their inventiveness and rampant curiosity, these rival scientists had opened the world's eyes to a whole new universe of living things. Suddenly, it seemed invisible cells were all around us at all times – even floating in their millions in apparently clear water and blooming between our teeth!

This was a massive discovery – but, as is usually the case in science, it unleashed a whole bucket-load of new questions. Most pressingly, if living cells are all over the place, where the heck do they come from? And, for that matter, where does life itself come from?

THE *SPONTANEOUS GENERATION* ZOMBIE

Across the world, people have long grown up listening to all kinds of traditional stories about how life on Earth got started.

Hawaiians believed it began when male and female spirits came together in an underwater cave.

The Kuba people of Central Africa thought life happened after a god with indigestion vomited up the sun, moon, stars and the very first creatures.

The Christian Bible, the Islamic Koran and many other holy books also provided creation stories, but many 17th- and 18th-century scientists preferred a 2,000-year-old explanation first put forward by Aristotle, a philosopher in ancient Greece.

BUT he thought completely lifeless substances like mud, clay and water, could suddenly create new life forms.

So Aristotle didn't believe that life started just once with Luca and his clan, he thought it kept on bubbling up again and again from lifeless matter.

In fact, just a few decades before Hooke and van Leeuwenhoek built their microscopes, a Dutch doctor called Jean Baptiste van Helmont did an experiment that he thought proved Aristotle was right. He reckoned he could show that things as big and complicated as mice were produced by spontaneous generation.

Van Helmont's Mouse-making Experiment

Ingredients:
1 dirty shirt
1 handful of grain
1 jar of air

Method:
1. Stick all the ingredients into the jar (no need to put a lid on it).
2. Leave them for 21 days.
3. Return to find new mice living happily in the jar.

The coast is clear!

Van Helmont was convinced the mice really had been spontaneously generated. But there's an easy way to prove he was wrong. Yup, all you've got to do is screw a lid on the jar tightly, so no mice can sneak in for a feast.

The spontaneous generation idea isn't actually as bonkers as it seems, though. Think about it. Moss appears on rocks, as if from nowhere. Weeds suddenly pop up out of cracks in the pavement. A clear pond can turn green with algae on a sunny day. And mould and bacteria suddenly appear on food when it rots.

Today, we know that these dramatic new flushes of life are always triggered by existing cells. Bacteria, algae and the *spores* that spread moulds and mosses are tiny cells that can waft in on a breeze. So can microscopic pieces of lichen and the minuscule seeds of many plants. Scientists and thinkers like Aristotle and van Helmont were incredibly clever people, but without the power of microscopes, nobody had any clue that all these tiny life forms even existed, and they certainly never imagined that invisible cells were floating around in the air we breathe, or inside our bodies.

Even after all those microscopic cells had been discovered, the spontaneous generation idea persisted way into the 19th century. Lots of scientists argued that van Leeuwenhoek's *'very wee animals'* were actually life forms that had emerged from non-living matter and were just starting to take shape.

In fact, rather like a zombie, the spontaneous generation theory refused to die. It survived for centuries, despite repeated attempts to use scientific evidence to kill it off.

CHAPTER 4
Wrestling with the Zombie
DO ALL CELLS COME FROM CELLS?

In 1855, nearly 200 years after Hooke first spotted those little cork cells, a German scientist called Rudolf Virchow thought he'd finally killed off the spontaneous generation zombie.

Virchow was a rather brilliant writer, historian, doctor and politician, as well as being a biologist – and a bit of a show-off. He took great delight in explaining his powerful new idea about the origins of all living cells with a simple phrase:

Omnis cellula e cellula.

Clever, isn't it?

Oh, sorry, not everyone learns Latin these days, do they?

Virchow was basically saying 'all cells come from cells'. It sounds simple enough, but this was a brand-new concept in the 19th century.

He hadn't come up with the idea all by himself. A lot of other scientists had been working on it for many years, including one of Virchow's less flashy colleagues, Robert Remak.

While Virchow was busily dabbling in lots of different areas, Remak stuck at just one thing: he watched living cells going about their business and he saw some really exciting stuff down his microscope.

He didn't ever spot a cell 'spontaneously generating', but he watched with amazement as new cells were born.

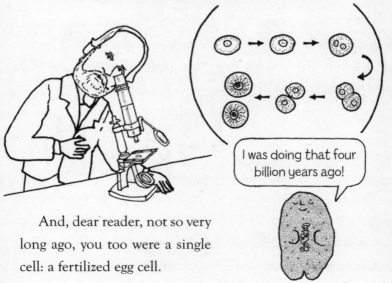

I was doing that four billion years ago!

And, dear reader, not so very long ago, you too were a single cell: a fertilized egg cell.

That cell divided in two again and again and again, until, eventually, you were born: a wriggling, writhing, living, breathing baby! You contained several trillion cells, and they all came from other cells.

Even the egg cell that started it all came from another cell: one in your (biological) mother's body. And the cells in her body started out as cells in your grandmother's body, and so on, further and further back in time. Every family is different. This is just how one baby's family line might look.

The line stretches all the way back to Luca – the ancestor we all have in common. Being able to reproduce by dividing one cell into two was Luca's superpower, of course, and nowadays, biologists have a name for that process . . .

Mitosis: How Cells Divide

Cells must go to great lengths to get *mitosis* just right. After all, their own survival and that of their future descendants depends on it. Cell division is a massive challenge, though. First, the cell has to make a copy of all its DNA genes, then it needs to divide them so both new cells contain a perfect set of operating instructions. If cells are born with bits of information missing, things can go badly wrong. That's how some cancers start, for example.

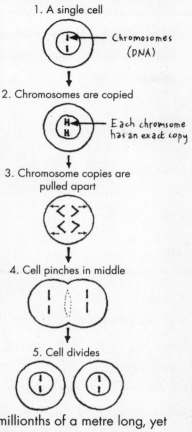

1. A single cell

Chromosomes (DNA)

2. Chromosomes are copied

Each chromsome has an exact copy

3. Chromosome copies are pulled apart

4. Cell pinches in middle

5. Cell divides

Each human cell is just a few millionths of a metre long, yet there are two metres of gene-carrying chromosomes (see p. 36) squeezed inside it. Every bit of that DNA has to be untangled, copied and packed into the two new cells that are formed by the cell that is dividing.

Imagine Cell City, from Chapter 2, constructing an exact, fully working copy of itself, inside itself, and then dividing into two complete working cities. As well as the DNA, all those other organelle 'buildings' need to be shared out between the two cells, so each new 'city' has all the 'services' it needs.

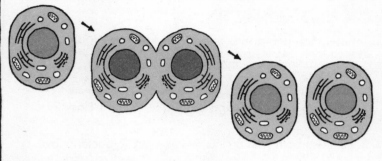

If cells didn't do all that, you wouldn't be here!

Mitosis was the process Remak saw happening down his microscope in the middle of the 19th century, and it's what keeps life going, growing and surviving for generation after generation.

Virchow's big idea – that cells only ever come from existing cells – supported by Remak's description of how cells actually divide, changed the way people thought about life. But was this explanation powerful enough to finally banish the spontaneous generation zombie?

The answer, as you've probably already guessed, is no.

A Killer Experiment

In horror movies, you can usually only stop a zombie by chopping off its head, maybe with a sword or a chainsaw. But when a French scientist called Louis Pasteur finally brought the spontaneous generation zombie to its knees in 1859, he used a very different sort of weapon: a clever experiment.

1. Take two flasks and label them 'Flask 1' and 'Flask 2'.

2. Fill them both with a clear chicken broth (bacteria love to grow in broth).

3. Heat the neck of Flask 1 in a flame and bend it into an S shape (so that air can get in, but anything heavier is kept out). Leave the neck of Flask 2 straight, and open to the air.

4. Boil the broth in both flasks for an hour to completely kill off all living bacteria cells that might be in the broth.

5. Wait and watch, to see if anything starts to grow in either flask.

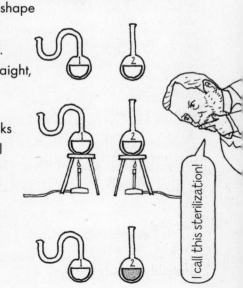

I call this sterilization!

Pasteur had designed this experiment very carefully. He had two different ideas, or predictions, about what might happen and he wanted the experiment to prove which one was right.

Prediction one If the spontaneous generation idea was right, and life really can appear from lifeless matter (i.e. the sterilized chicken broth), then bacteria and mould will eventually grow in BOTH flasks.

OR

Prediction two If Remak and Virchow were right, and cells only ever come from other cells, then bacteria would only grow in the straight-necked Flask 2. That's because bacteria and spores that are floating around in the air could fall into Flask 2, but they COULD NOT fall into the bent-necked Flask 1.

The beauty of the experiment was that these predictions couldn't both be true. So what did Pasteur see? Here's what happened:

Within a couple of days, Flask 2, with its neck open to the air, became murky, and probably quite smelly, as bacteria flourished in the rich chicken broth.

But the bent-necked Flask 1 stayed completely clear. Pasteur waited . . . and waited . . . and waited. There were no signs of life. Not a sausage (well, perhaps that's not a surprise). Not a single bacteria cell appeared.

Prediction two was the winner. Pasteur was convinced that he'd finally killed the zombie!

Excited by the success of his experiment, he declared:

> The doctrine of spontaneous generation will never recover from the mortal blow inflicted by this experiment.

Dead Zombie Saves Millions of Lives

Pasteur's clever experiment didn't just bring us closer to the true story of how life works, it also helped save many millions of human lives.

If his name sounds familiar, that might be because the milk and the orange juice on your breakfast table have been 'pasteurized'. To pasteurize a substance, instead of boiling the liquid hard, like he had in the two-flask experiment, Pasteur worked out how to use gentler heat to kill off bacteria that can exist in food, like dairy produce, and make it go off. This made the food last much longer without ruining the taste. And with that one action, Pasteur helped prevent billions of cases of food poisoning.

But he did even more than that.

In Pasteur's day, people had all sorts of crazy-sounding theories about what made them ill. Some of the most popular beliefs included bad air; imbalances of the 'four humours' (blood, phlegm, black bile and yellow bile – said to flow through the body); and curses, spells or punishments from the heavens. If you had no clue that invisible cells existed, and that tiny living beasts could break into your body and make you feel sick, you might well believe them too.

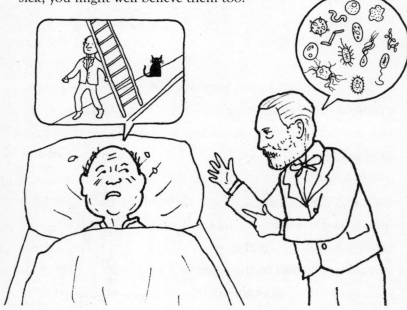

Pasteur, on the other hand, was convinced that all infectious diseases are caused by microscopic living beings. This idea was called 'germ theory' and Pasteur spent the rest of his life proving it was true, and using it to save even more lives by finding ways to tackle the germs themselves. He:

• Invented several vaccines that protected people and animals from infectious diseases caused by bacteria and viruses (tiny *parasites* that reproduce themselves by hijacking other living cells).

• And kick-started a great hunt for the first antibiotics, which are medicines that work by killing bacteria without harming our cells.

Today, thanks to the work of Pasteur and many others since, vaccines and antibiotics save millions of lives every single day.

Even so, it wasn't until the beginning of the 20th century, that most scientists and doctors accepted that living germs really do cause infectious diseases. Unfortunately for Pasteur, he was already dead by then.

Pasteur didn't just banish the spontaneous generation zombie, he changed the world with a couple of glass flasks, some chicken soup and a brilliant idea.

Your good health!

Sorry, Luca, but, truth be told, if it wasn't for the zombie, you wouldn't be here. In fact, none of us would.

We already know that the cells in your body are all related to Luca, the first proper cell.

But what came before Luca? How was Luca made? At some point, way, way back in time, something lifeless must have come to life for the first time. So how on earth did it all begin?

It was me, I started it all! That's what I keep trying to tell you.

Hmm, well, actually that makes some kind of sense. Spontaneous generation might not be happening right now, but it must have happened at least once during the long history of our planet.

Basically, a bunch of different chemicals must have started bumping into each other and reacting with each other.

Quite simple chemical reactions probably built up gradually and got more and more complex.

Over time, various different reactions would have started to rely on each other to keep themselves going.

Eventually, a whole set of reactions must have become dependent on each other and started to behave a bit like a living thing. By working together, they could maintain themselves, reproduce themselves and spread. Finally, millions of years later, these reactions turned into a cell: Luca.

Ta-da!

When it comes to working out precisely how and when all the pieces of a living cell fell into place, scientists have got very little actual evidence to work with.

When palaeontologists want to find out about dinosaurs, they can look at fossils that built up more than 65 million years ago, before these giant reptiles became extinct.

Believe it or not, the cells of bacteria can also be fossilized, but they're much, much harder to find and interpret. And, unfortunately, fossils from Luca's day are not going to show up, however hard we look. That's mainly because there are barely any rocks old enough to find them in! Almost all the rocks that formed four billion years ago have since been worn away, smashed up by meteorite strikes or forced down into the planet's molten mantle, taking any traces of life with them.

This shortage of direct evidence makes it very, very tricky to work out how the first cells came to be, but, amazingly, scientists haven't been put off by this.

COOKING UP SOME FOUR-BILLION-YEAR-OLD SOUP

One of the first people to start thinking about the very beginnings of life on Earth was Charles Darwin – who shocked the world with his theory of evolution by natural selection, which suggested humans and all other apes had evolved from the same ape-like ancestor. Many people were horrified enough by that theory, so when Darwin proposed in 1871 that life as a whole might have started out as simple chemicals floating around in a 'warm little pond', his new idea was even more shocking.

It wasn't until 70 years after Darwin died that a young scientist called Stanley Miller decided to actually test out the idea in a chemistry lab. By then most people had accepted that life really had evolved from much simpler beginnings, and some scientists were calling that starting point the 'primordial soup'*.

* 'Primordial' means 'at the beginning of time'.

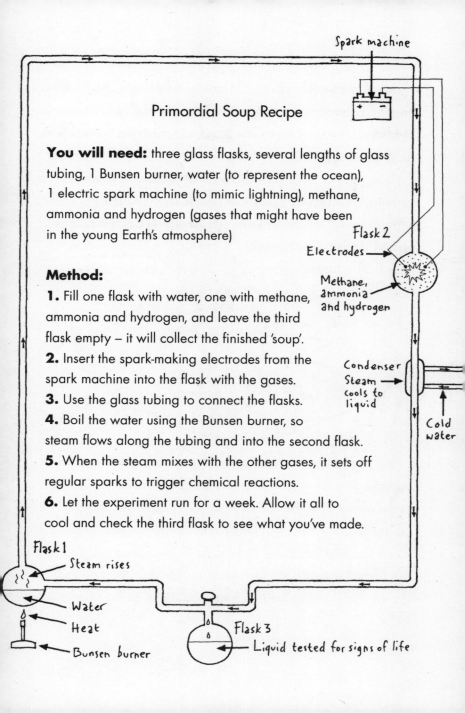

Primordial Soup Recipe

You will need: three glass flasks, several lengths of glass tubing, 1 Bunsen burner, water (to represent the ocean), 1 electric spark machine (to mimic lightning), methane, ammonia and hydrogen (gases that might have been in the young Earth's atmosphere)

Method:

1. Fill one flask with water, one with methane, ammonia and hydrogen, and leave the third flask empty – it will collect the finished 'soup'.

2. Insert the spark-making electrodes from the spark machine into the flask with the gases.

3. Use the glass tubing to connect the flasks.

4. Boil the water using the Bunsen burner, so steam flows along the tubing and into the second flask.

5. When the steam mixes with the other gases, it sets off regular sparks to trigger chemical reactions.

6. Let the experiment run for a week. Allow it all to cool and check the third flask to see what you've made.

Spark machine

Flask 2

Electrodes

Methane, ammonia and hydrogen

Condenser
Steam cools to liquid

Cold water

Flask 1

Steam rises

Water

Heat

Bunsen burner

Flask 3

Liquid tested for signs of life

Is your mouth watering? Hmmm, maybe not. Apart from anything, the raw ingredients aren't very appealing – ammonia is the stuff that makes pee smell bad and methane is one of the main gases in farts.

But, tasty or not, when Miller took a look at what kind of chemicals his finished soup contained, he could hardly believe what he saw. Dissolved in the pale, reddish-brown liquid were several different substances called *amino acids*.

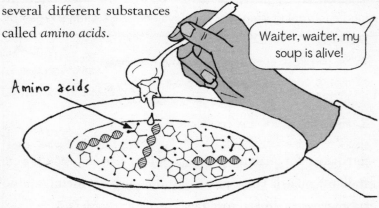

Waiter, waiter, my soup is alive!

Amino acids

Amino acids are extremely important to all life forms because they are the chemical building blocks that cells use to make proteins in their ribosomes (see p. 38). Ribosomes link amino acids together in a long chain that then folds up to form a new protein. You can't make cells without proteins, and you can't make proteins without amino acids. So they were exactly the kind of thing Miller had hoped he'd find in his primordial soup.

It was an exciting discovery, but making amino acids was just a start.

Believe it or not, these two sentences . . .

> When using language and making proteins, order is everything.

and

> iuhd e,inls antug irrnaneaoeg raevmongheeyk t.iidng Wgssprn

. . . are made up from exactly the same set of letters and punctuation marks. But by jumbling up the order, the whole sentence becomes completely meaningless.

Just like the second sentence, Miller's soup had all the right ingredients for making proteins, but the amino acids were randomly mixed. For a protein to do anything useful, amino acids have to be linked together in a specific order.

In a living cell genes act like the 'writer' making sense of the amino acid 'letters' and each gene contains a code that spells out a protein 'word' or 'words'.

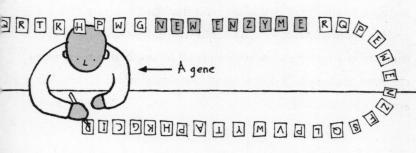

← A gene

Unfortunately, Miller hadn't cooked up anything that looked remotely like genes, so creating working proteins from the amino acids he'd discovered was, as one scientist put it, about as likely as the idea that a tornado could sweep through a junkyard and put together a jet plane.

When the soup didn't turn up all the answers, scientists started looking elsewhere for clues.

According to one theory, life might have started in some other part of our galaxy, arrived here part-formed, then carried on evolving down here on Earth into what it is today. Complex chemicals, including amino acids, have actually been found inside meteorites that have landed on Earth.

I am not an alien!

But then scientists found some intriguing clues that led them towards a more believable explanation. You can see this evidence for yourself, but only if you jump into a submarine and head down to the bottom of the ocean.

Depth

CLUES FROM THE LOST CITY

All aboard? Our mission is to investigate part of the seabed called the Atlantis Massif, right out in the very middle of the Atlantic Ocean. Ready? Let's dive.

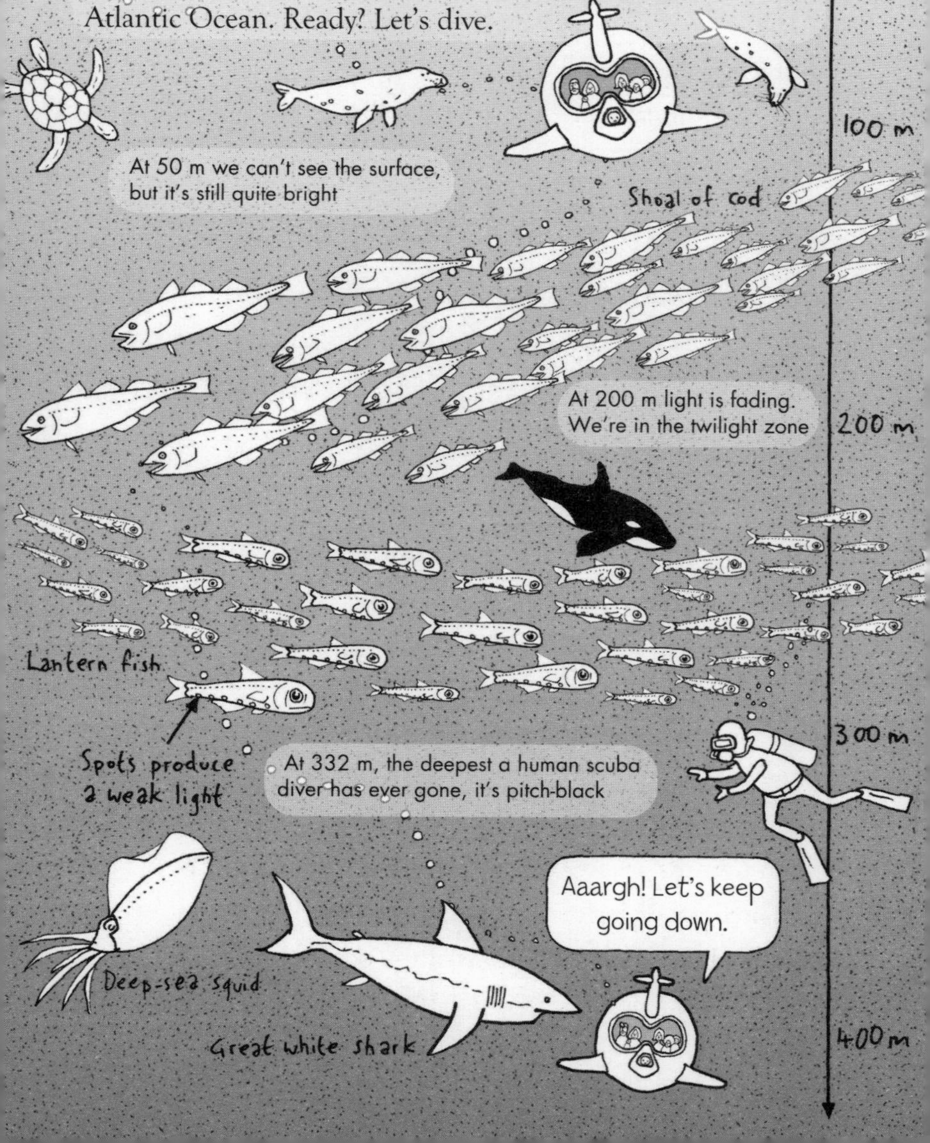

100 m

At 50 m we can't see the surface, but it's still quite bright

Shoal of cod

At 200 m light is fading. We're in the twilight zone

200 m

Lantern fish

300 m

Spots produce a weak light

At 332 m, the deepest a human scuba diver has ever gone, it's pitch-black

Aaargh! Let's keep going down.

Deep-sea squid

Great white shark

400 m

Six gill shark

Analyzing the seawater for signs of microscopic life, we can see it's absolutely jam-packed with bacteria and archaea cells. That must be why it looks so cloudy.

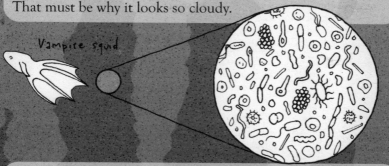
Vampire squid

Let's hurry back up to the surface and make sense of this weird place.

This journey really happened on 4th December 2000, except there weren't any humans on board the sub. The scientists in charge of the mission watched in awe as their remote-controlled submarine's cameras revealed a completely new kind of deep-sea world. Most of the ocean floor is a cold, boring desert, but this part of the Atlantis Massif was teeming with life, and some of the stone chimneys were as tall as 18-storey tower blocks. No wonder the scientists called it the Lost City.

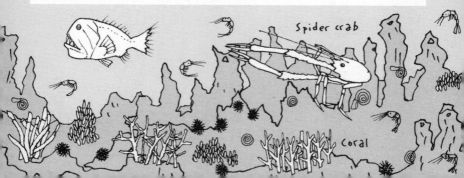
Spider crab

Coral

THE LOST CITY HYDROTHERMAL VENT

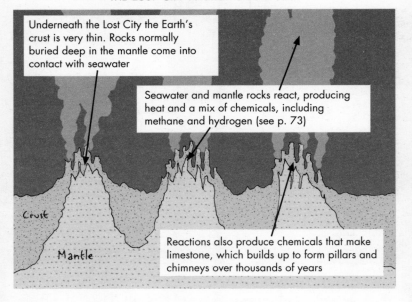

Underneath the Lost City the Earth's crust is very thin. Rocks normally buried deep in the mantle come into contact with seawater

Seawater and mantle rocks react, producing heat and a mix of chemicals, including methane and hydrogen (see p. 73)

Crust

Mantle

Reactions also produce chemicals that make limestone, which builds up to form pillars and chimneys over thousands of years

THE ZOMBIE'S SECRET RECIPE

If Stanley Miller's primordial soup was no more than a thin, watery starter course, some scientists are convinced that places like the Lost City contain everything needed to cook up the full meal: actual living cells.

There are four crucial ingredients needed to make cells, and deep-sea *alkaline* hydrothermal vents have plenty of all of them.

Energy

• **Ingredient 1: a rich mixture of chemicals** The water around these vents is more like a hearty stew of different chemical substances. It's got all the elements needed to build the proteins, nucleic acids, carbohydrates and lipids that cells are made from (see pp. 32-33).

• **Ingredient 2: energy** There's loads of energy around the vents, thanks to all that heat from the constantly reacting mantle rocks. Those reactions also make hydrogen. Almost all living cells use electrically charged hydrogen atoms, called protons, to capture energy and turn it into ATP (see p. 44), so it's a good bet that the very first lifelike forms were powered by hydrogen too.

• **Ingredient 3: a protective shell** Today's cells use lipid membranes for this, but at first tiny bubbles or pores in the rock round hydrothermal vents might have done a similar job.

• **Ingredient 4: catalysts* to kick-start reactions** That's the job enzymes do for cells nowadays, but they weren't there at the beginning. Instead it's likely that metal atoms, such as iron, which were embedded in the rocks around the vent, helped get all sorts of chemical reactions fizzing.

* A catalyst is something that speeds up a specific chemical reaction, without itself being changed by the reaction.

Those are the vital ingredients, the deep-sea hydrothermal vent was the kitchen and the spontaneous generation zombie was the chef. Unfortunately, the actual recipe the zombie followed to make the first cells is still a closely guarded secret.

Scientists are working hard to pick away at this mystery. They keep coming up with good ideas, they just need to agree with each other!

Genes must have come before cells. They're the instructions that have to be passed on every time a cell divides.

But I can make lipid molecules from scratch. They assemble into bubbles spontaneously. I say the membrane wrapper came first.

Rubbish, genes can't copy themselves without proteins. Some kind of enzyme must have come first.

The honest truth is, nobody really knows how the first cell came to be. And as any good cook will tell you, the best way to perfect a recipe is to keep on experimenting until you get it right.

Scientists haven't really managed to knock up anything very lifelike yet. After all, it took millions of years of experimentation before life itself could get going. But maybe one day they'll whip up some chemical reactions that can keep going and reproduce themselves. And if they manage to do that, we'll finally understand the spontaneous generation zombie's extraordinary skills.

They're not having my secret recipe!

We still don't know exactly how Luca was made. But we do know that once cell-based life got started, there was no stopping it.

Prepare to be amazed!

CHAPTER 6
Revolution!
The Tiny Cells that Changed the Whole World

After all that talk of vents and catalysts and zombies in the last chapter, we might need to slow things down a little. So let's take a deep breath.

Inhale slowly and count up to seven: one, two . . . three . . . four . . . five . . . six . . . seven.

Hold it for one . . . two . . . three.

And now breathe out slowly: one . . . two . . . three . . . four . . . five . . . six . . . seven.

Feel good? All that lovely oxygen filling your lungs and running through your bloodstream is so calming.

About a fifth of the air we breathe is oxygen. All the cells in your body – and in most plants and animals alive today – rely on the stuff. Mitochondria need it to extract energy from

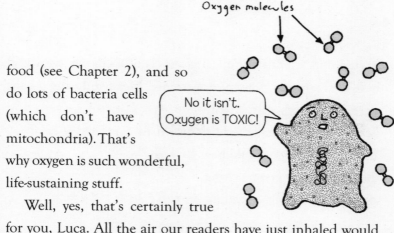

food (see Chapter 2), and so do lots of bacteria cells (which don't have mitochondria). That's why oxygen is such wonderful, life-sustaining stuff.

No it isn't. Oxygen is TOXIC!

Well, yes, that's certainly true for you, Luca. All the air our readers have just inhaled would have killed you instantly.

But there was practically no oxygen gas in the atmosphere at all for the first two billion years of Earth's history. That changed when a new kind of cell arrived. It was absolutely minute, but it bloomed in such monumentally massive numbers that it transformed most cellular life for good. How? By releasing oxygen into the air, as we'll see on page 88.

Actually, this wasn't the first time cells had flourished so well that they'd altered the whole planet. During the first two billion years, different waves of life forms rose and fell. Like hordes of tiny artists (wielding even tinier paintbrushes) they changed the colour scheme of the entire planet several times over.

1. The Orange and Green Planet (4.5–3.4 billion years ago)

Nothing with eyes was around to see the planet when life first started, but scientists think high levels of methane gas would have made the sky glow an eerie orange. Meanwhile, the oceans were awash with dissolved iron atoms. Without oxygen, iron doesn't react to make reddish-brown rust, instead it creates a 'green rust', which would have turned the seas a yucky green colour.

2. The Purple Planet (~3.4–2.5 billion years ago)

Up until now, life forms had probably gathered most of their energy from geological activity, like the hydrothermal vent that kept Luca going. Or they might have scavenged waste products made by other cells.

But then some of Luca's descendants managed to capture energy from the sun. That's what green plants and algae do

86

today, of course, through a process called *photosynthesis*. But 3.4 billion years ago it was a massive new development. Life no longer had to cluster round deep-sea vents. Instead it could bloom all over the ocean, and move much closer to the surface. These new blooms weren't like plants or seaweeds, though –

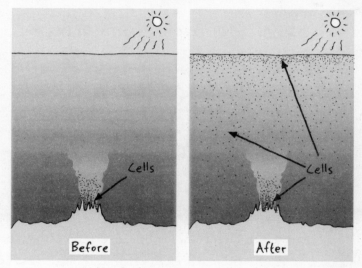

they weren't even green. Instead they were purple-coloured archaea cells! And some scientists think they may have been so successful that they turned the seas purple too.

3. A Splash of Blood Red (~2.6–2.4 billion years ago)

This is where those new cells that first started pumping out oxygen came onto the scene. They were a group of bacteria, called *cyanobacteria*, that had developed an even more powerful way of using the sun's energy. They were the first cells to produce a bright green substance, called *chlorophyll*, which made them look bright green and triggered a new and highly efficient version of the chemical reaction known as ...

Photosynthesis

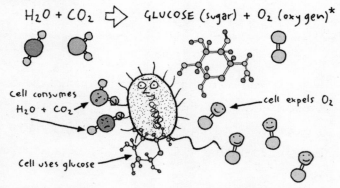

$$H_2O + CO_2 \Rightarrow GLUCOSE \text{ (sugar)} + O_2 \text{ (oxygen)}^*$$

Cell consumes $H_2O + CO_2$

cell expels O_2

Cell uses glucose

These cells separated water molecules (H_2O) into hydrogen (H) and oxygen (O). They combined the hydrogen with carbon dioxide gas (CO_2) to make energy-rich carbohydrates, but the oxygen was a waste product; they let that bubble away.

As we know, oxygen can be dangerous stuff. Because its atoms are highly reactive, it quickly binds to other elements, like hydrogen (to make water) or carbon (to make carbon dioxide gas). Oxygen is so determined to get hold of those partner atoms that it can rip them out of other molecules, including the ones found in cells. This can cause serious damage to a

* This is the exact reverse of the respiration reaction on page 44.

cell's most important equipment, including its proteins and DNA. Even today, although your cells need oxygen to survive, they handle it with great care.

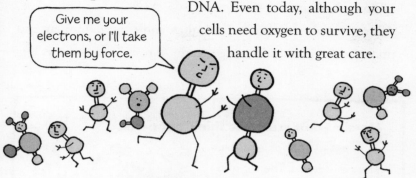

Oxygen is mad keen on binding with iron and there was a lot of that left over from the planet's orange and green phase. With oxygen released into the water, the iron atoms now oxidized to a reddish-brown rust, turning the oceans the colour of blood.

Thousands of different *species* of cyanobacteria (also called blue-green algae, though they're bacteria, not algae) are still found all over the place today, thriving pretty much wherever there's water and sunlight. They actually produce a significant chunk of the oxygen we breathe.

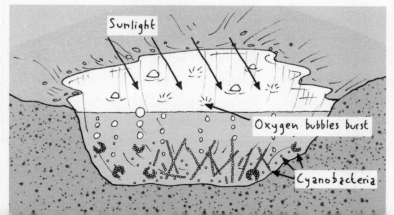

4. The Ice-White, Nearly Dead Snowball Planet (~2.4–2.1 billion years ago)

All the newly formed oxygen that came bubbling out of photosynthesizing cells very nearly wrecked everything for everyone.

Here's what scientists think happened:

1. Those cyanobacteria were mass murderers. The oxygen they produced poisoned other life forms on a scale never witnessed before or since.

2. To fuel their photosynthesis, the cyanobacteria soaked up a huge amount of carbon dioxide from the atmosphere. Since carbon dioxide is a greenhouse gas (i.e. it traps heat in the planet's atmosphere), this was the opposite of global warming. The planet started to get colder.

3. Oxygen reacted with the methane that had been in the air since the planet first formed, breaking it down into water and carbon dioxide. This turned the orange sky blue. But, since methane is an even more powerful greenhouse gas than carbon dioxide, the reduced level of methane meant the planet grew even colder.

4. As these processes continued, the effects got stronger and the planet kept on growing colder. Eventually, the temperature dropped as low as -50 °C and the entire surface of the planet was covered in a thick layer of ice. For the next 300 million years, Earth was a giant white snowball spinning through space.

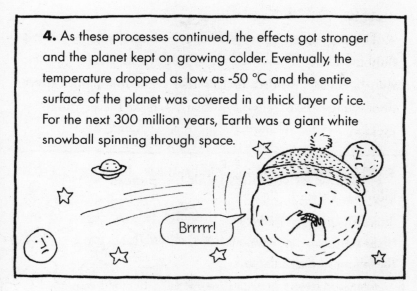

Brrrrr!

Over its long history, life on Earth has survived some pretty rough patches, but this might have been the lowest point of all. Some scientists call this period the Great Oxygen Catastrophe, because oxygen was a complete and utter disaster for most living things. Oxygen even killed off most of the cyanobacteria that had created it – they'd effectively poisoned and iced over their own home!

You idiots! You killed most other living cells, and most of yourselves too. What were you thinking?!

The truth was, of course, that the cyanobacteria weren't thinking at all. They were minuscule single-celled *organisms*, with no brains, so they had no way of knowing what effect they were having or when to stop.

They very nearly snuffed life out altogether.

5. The Boring, Stinking Sludge-Black Planet (~2.1–0.8 billion years ago)

Nobody is quite sure how they did it, but cell-based life survived. And eventually, after 300 million long, freezing years, the snowball Earth thawed out.

Some scattered populations of cells that had managed to survive, perhaps by hanging out near hydrothermal vents, inside blocks of ice or in any available puddles of non-frozen water, emerged into a new and totally different world. Oxygen was here to stay, although there was  still much less of it in the atmosphere than there is today. Cells had a choice: hide out and try to avoid oxygen, or find new ways to live with it and use it.

This was quite a challenge, so life didn't joyously rush back to fill the warmer planet. Change happened really slowly.

So slowly, in fact, that some scientists call the next phase of planetary life the 'Boring Billion'. It lasted for nearly a quarter of the planet's entire history!

The oceans turned murky and dark. And it's lucky nothing living had a sense of smell back then, because the whole place would have reeked worse than a mountain of rotten eggs in the middle of a sewage works. That's because the seas were chock-full of bacteria and archaea that fed on chemical substances containing sulphur – which meant they burped out huge clouds of hydrogen sulphide. That's the gas that gives bad eggs, sewage and farts their . . . er . . . distinctive aroma. It's also corrosive, highly flammable and poisonous to many other life forms.

But living cells have an amazing way of turning a problem – such as the arrival of another highly toxic new gas – into an opportunity. Some kinds of cyanobacteria did very well for themselves by developing a way to use hydrogen sulphide, instead of water, to fuel their photosynthesis.

The Boring Billion may not have smelled great, and the *microbes* that lived there might've painted it a pretty drab and unpleasant colour, but it actually wasn't boring at all.

There still weren't any fish in the sea, birds in the sky, or animals on land. Up until this point in our planet's history the single-celled bacteria and archaea were the only forms of life that existed. But during this period another completely new and powerful cell arrived on the scene. Bacteria and archaea didn't have the whole place to themselves any more, and the stage was set for a new generation of larger and more complex life forms. It was this new kind of cell that would go on to redecorate the whole place yet again, eventually turning it into the green and pleasant planet that we live on today.

CHAPTER 7
New Cell on the Block
How Two Merging Cells Changed Life For Ever

One day, approximately two billion years ago, two cells met. It couldn't have been love at first sight, but nevertheless, they hugged each other tight, pooled their resources and, eventually, moved in together.

I'm awesome!

In doing this, they rolled their two separate lives into one, creating a completely new kind of cell – a supercharged cell, with new powers and all kinds of exciting new adventures ahead of it.

As usual, when trying to reconstruct events that happened such a very long time ago, there's very little direct proof. But biologists pieced together lots of clues and came up with a theory.

How Two Cells Became One

1. Around two billion years ago, all life forms were single-celled microbes:

Bacteria and archaea

2. Oxygen levels were rising, with dangerous consequences for lots of cells.

3. Some bacteria worked out how to use oxygen to turn food into ATP, the crucial battery-like molecule that powers all cells (called cellular respiration, see p. 44).

4. One of those bacteria bumped into an archaea cell, and the two different cells started to swap goodies. This worked out well for both partners.

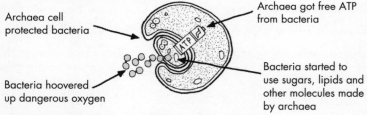

Archaea cell protected bacteria

Archaea got free ATP from bacteria

Bacteria hoovered up dangerous oxygen

Bacteria started to use sugars, lipids and other molecules made by archaea

5. Eventually, the two cells merged into one.

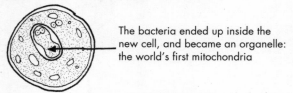

The bacteria ended up inside the new cell, and became an organelle: the world's first mitochondria

6. Both partners stopped being independent cells and created another world-changing first: the eukaryote cell.

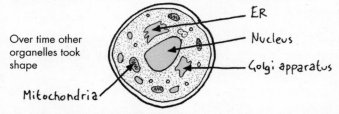

Over time other organelles took shape

ER

Nucleus

Golgi apparatus

Mitochondria

Once eukaryote cells entered the scene, life on Earth changed for ever.

You are made from eukaryote cells, remember, so without that coming together of cells two thousand million years ago, you wouldn't be here now. We wouldn't have the Amazon rainforest, flocks of migrating swallows or giant squid the size of buses. And there certainly wouldn't be anything that even vaguely resembles the brain you're using to decipher the words on this page.

CELLS GET A TURBO BOOST

If there's one single thing that allowed eukaryote cells to evolve into so many amazing living structures, it was probably the arrival of their mitochondria. As far as we're aware, no bacteria or archaea have anything remotely like mitochondria that make ATP *inside* their cells. Instead the membrane that's wrapped round the *outside* of their cells produces those vital, energy-carrying ATP molecules.

It's not just that they've never evolved mitochondria and other organelles; nearly all archaea and bacteria cells have remained microscopically tiny throughout their four-billion-year history. Many biologists think these two facts –

97

the cells' smallness and overall simplicity – are closely connected.

It's all to do with something called surface-area-to-volume ratio, and to understand that, brace yourselves, we need to do a little bit of maths.

Here's how a small bacteria cell uses its cell membrane to make ATP.

• If the cell grows to double its original size, the volume inside it increases roughly eight times. So it needs about eight times more ATP molecules to keep it going.

• But the space covered by its membrane has only increased four times. To make enough ATP, it has to fill its entire membrane with ATP-making enzymes.

• If the cell doubles in size again, to four times its original size, it would need around 64 times more ATP than the original small cell, but its membrane area would only have grown by 16 times. There's simply not enough space to make all that ATP. The cell soon runs out of energy. It definitely can't grow any bigger.

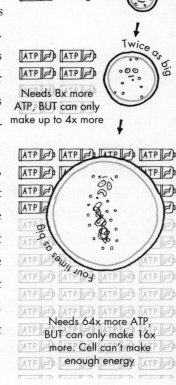

A single cell

Twice as big

Needs 8x more ATP, BUT can only make up to 4x more

Four times as big

Needs 64x more ATP, BUT can only make 16x more. Cell can't make enough energy

Now look at this small cell that contains mitochondria to make ATP on the inside. ──────▶

• If the cell grows to double its original size, it can just make more or bigger mitochondria.

• If it doubles in size again, it can satisfy its need for energy by making even more mitochondria.

• These cells can grow much bigger with lots of ──────▶ mitochondria.

The appearance of mitochondria didn't only allow eukaryote cells to get bigger, it also meant they could get much more complicated.

If a cell builds internal structures, like organelles and complex cytoskeletons, it needs to produce a wider range of proteins to construct and operate all that fancy new machinery. But more proteins means more genes and an awful lot more energy. Providing all that energy isn't an option for microbes that can only make their ATP with their cell membranes, but it's not really a problem for a cell that can build itself more mitochondria 'power stations'.

For example, the muscle cells in your heart contain complex spring-like structures that need to contract and relax again and again, 24 hours a day, seven days a week, in order to keep your heart beating. Doing that takes a huge amount of ATP, which is why some of those cells contain a phenomenal 5,000 mitochondria.

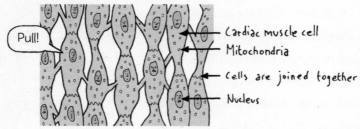

Pull!

Cardiac muscle cell
Mitochondria
Cells are joined together
Nucleus

CLUES IN THE CHROMOSOMES

Of course, biologists aren't absolutely certain how all this happened. They argue a lot about when, where and how the first eukaryote cells came into being. But if they want to have any chance of proving a particular theory is true, they have to gather every scrap of evidence they can.

I don't consider my ideas controversial. I consider them right.

The first biologist to argue forcefully that mitochondria were once separate cells in their own right, was Lynn Margulis. Scientists usually share their ideas and results with the world by writing them up in a scientific paper that will then be published in a scientific journal for other scientists to read. Margulis wrote her paper in the late 1960s, and it was full of great data and arguments, but it was rejected by the editors of fifteen different scientific journals before it finally got published. Why? Because the editors thought the idea of one living cell ending up inside another living cell and staying there for good sounded just too ridiculous to be true. When Margulis applied for a grant so she could investigate her idea further, one expert who assessed her application told her it was 'crap'. Charming!

Luckily, Margulis wasn't put off. She had faith in the evidence she'd gathered and carried on with her research regardless. More than 10 years later, other scientists finally started to accept that her incredible idea was almost certainly true.

Eukaryote cells keep all their main chromosomes in their nucleus, but Margulis knew mitochondria contained a separate, smaller chromosome of their own. Pictures taken with powerful electron microscopes showed that the mitochondria's chromosome looked like the chromosome of a bacteria cell, but Margulis couldn't actually prove it was until she could read the genes in the chromosome. And it simply wasn't possible to do that when she wrote that first paper.

Then, early in the 1970s, scientists finally invented a way to sequence DNA, which meant they could decipher the code of genes. In 1978, DNA sequencing showed that mitochondria genes are very, very similar to the genes of certain kinds of free-living bacteria that still exist today.

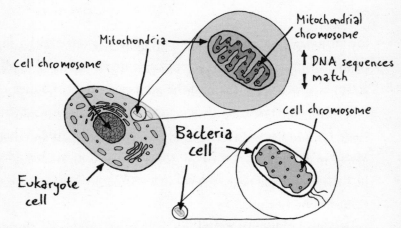

Mitochondria

Cell chromosome

Mitochondrial chromosome

↑ DNA sequences ↓ match

Bacteria cell

Cell chromosome

Eukaryote cell

This answer fitted perfectly with Margulis's explanation: mitochondria were once independent bacteria that moved in, set themselves up inside another cell, and never left. How else could an entire chromosome full of genes from bacteria possibly have ended up inside mitochondria?

AND THEN IT HAPPENED AGAIN!

Biologists call the cell-merging process that made mitochondria *endosymbiosis*. It seems to be an incredibly rare event. So rare, in fact, that mitochondria have only successfully formed once in the entire four billion years that life has existed on Earth. We know that's true because DNA sequencing shows that the genes in all the mitochondria in all eukaryotes, including all plants, animals and fungi, are extremely similar. They must all trace their roots back to the same original merging of cells.

Margulis had another theory about the origin of a different

world-changing organelle. She thought that chloroplasts in plant and algae cells, which turn the sun's energy into food (see p. 47), might also be the result of an ancient endosymbiosis.

Once again, DNA sequencing proved that she was absolutely right. Chloroplasts also have their own chromosomes and their genes match the DNA of photosynthesizing cyanobacteria, like the ones that nearly wiped out life in the Great Oxygen Catastrophe (see pp. 90-91).

About 1.5 billion years ago, a cyanobacteria cell started living inside a eukaryote cell, and produced yet another new and powerful kind of cell*.

These cells had their own power stations (mitochondria) **and** solar-powered farms (chloroplasts).

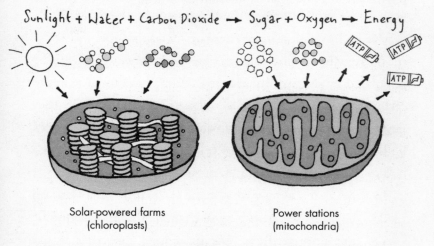

Sunlight + Water + Carbon Dioxide → Sugar + Oxygen → Energy

Solar-powered farms
(chloroplasts)

Power stations
(mitochondria)

---

*The kind of endosymbiosis that made chloroplasts is not quite so rare, it has happened on a few separate occasions since this first merger.

These new eukaryote cells were more self-sufficient than earlier cells had been. Eventually, they would blanket the whole world in grasses and trees and fill the sunlit parts of the lakes, rivers and oceans with seaweeds and algae.

Sometimes I'm just so proud of what my descendants have achieved. That's awesome.

It absolutely is.

We don't know all the details of how eukaryote cells acquired these new organelles, but, more than half a century after Lynn Margulis first proposed her new theory, we can be sure that her big idea was basically right. Endosymbiosis events seem to be exceedingly rare, but when they have happened – and lasted – they've had a revolutionary effect on life as a whole.

Without endosymbiosis, it's likely our planet would only be populated by single-celled bacteria and archaea today. They're certainly impressive little cells, but over four billion years they never truly succeeded in organizing themselves into complex bodies, with different types of cell in different parts of those bodies doing completely different things.

In time, that's exactly what some eukaryotic cells went on to do. As you'll see in the next chapter, the endosymbiotic events that formed these cells lit a long fuse that would eventually set off an explosion of *multicellular* life forms.

CHAPTER 8
Building Bigger Bodies
CELLS WORKING TOGETHER ACHIEVE WONDERFUL THINGS

The cells in your body are truly amazing. They are your most devoted servants and they work tirelessly, 24 hours a day, seven days a week, for your own personal benefit.

You contain trillions of them, and each and every one has its role to play. Cells built the bones, muscles and sinews that made it possible for you to climb out of bed this morning and take a big stretch.

Whenever you breathe in, cells in your lungs seize their chance to soak up oxygen from the air. They pass it on to red blood cells, which race through your blood vessels, delivering that crucial gas to every other cell in your body. As they go, they pick up and remove carbon dioxide waste.

After you swallow your breakfast toast, it's cells in your stomach and small intestine that do the work of digesting it and absorbing its nutritious goodness. Cells that make up your large intestine even get rid of the waste matter that's left over.

Billions of other cells make it their mission to protect the rest of your body, come what may. The white blood cells of your *immune system* are constantly on the lookout for intruders and damage. When they sense trouble, these cells swoop in to sort it out.

And thanks to the amazing way cells in your brain are constantly chattering between themselves, you can really feel that warm glow when morning sun lights up your face.

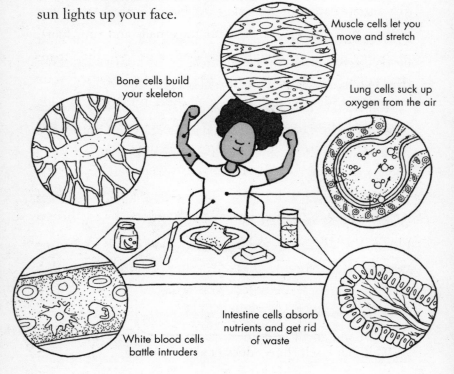

Muscle cells let you move and stretch

Bone cells build your skeleton

Lung cells suck up oxygen from the air

White blood cells battle intruders

Intestine cells absorb nutrients and get rid of waste

Your cells do all this, and much more besides, without ever asking to be paid for their services or needing to be told what to do (that's probably just as well, actually – imagine how stressful it would be if you had to remind your heart when to beat or your kidneys to filter your blood!). So committed are your cells to your personal well-being, that thousands of millions of them are willing to die for you every single day.

As you sit here reading this book, a constant stream of microscopic flakes of ex-skin cells are dropping off your body (the surface layers of your skin are basically made from the remains of dead cells, as are your fingernails and your hair). Every day around ten billion cells (that's more cells than there are people on the whole planet) from the lining of your intestine decide it's time to end it all. And just in the time it's taken you to read this page, more than 100,000,000 of your red blood cells will have worn themselves out and died, after three months of relentless hard work carrying oxygen round your body.

Fortunately for you, your body is always making new cells to replace the ones that are constantly dying. But why are they so willing to sacrifice themselves?

> Suckers! They're too busy looking after you to worry about looking after themselves.

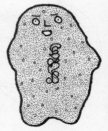

Well, Luca, selfishness doesn't always pay off.

Think of a factory building complex things like smartphones. The job is broken down into hundreds of different steps, with workers and robots trained or programmed to focus on particular tasks. That way, phones get built faster and to the same high standard. And anyway, no single worker could ever learn how to build every part of a complete smartphone on their own.

It's the same with cells. By combining lots of them together, with each one focusing on a specific task – to make a multicellular organism – living creatures can do things that one cell on its own could never dream of. That's how life produced 100-metre-tall redwood trees, as well as eagles, whose feathered wings help them fly high above those giant treetops.

A honey fungus in the blue mountains of Oregon, USA, is the biggest single living thing on Earth. It spreads through the soil across a 2,200-acre patch of land (about 1,250 football pitches!) and is estimated to be over 2,000 years old. How did it achieve its record-breaking status? Multicellularity.

Cells spotted the benefits of living together a very long time ago, way before eukaryotes came along. In fact, some of the oldest fossils of all are mushroom-shaped things called stromatolites, some of which lived around 3.5 billion years ago.

How Stromatolites Are Made

Cyanobacteria create sticky protein, carbohydrate and nucleic acid molecules

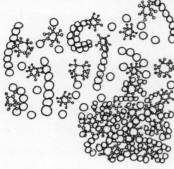

Molecules help gum billions of cyanobacteria together ➔ Each bacterial cell is tiny, but stromatolites can grow as big as an armchair!

Stromatolites form what scientists call a *biofilm*. Lots of different microbes form other kinds of biofilm today. They make:

• Those slippery layers on riverbed stones.

• The coatings of mould that float on top of long-forgotten cups of juice.

• And, if you've ever had tonsilitis, the bacteria that caused your sore throat probably formed a biofilm so they could cling on tight to your tonsils.

Biofilm! Sounds like the story of my life!

By working together to make a biofilm, individual cells are protected from the environment. So, for example, they don't dry out, get washed away or frazzled by the sun.

Biofilms are pretty amazing, but they're not nearly as fancy and well organized as true multicellular creatures, like us. It took a very, very long time for multicellular animals, plants and fungi to evolve, however. If the entire history of life on Earth had played out in a single week, starting on a Monday, the first single-celled eukaryotes didn't arrive until Thursday, then the first multicellular animals, plants or fungi turned up on Sunday morning. Our species only just nipped in before the end of the week, arriving a few seconds before midnight on Sunday night! (See p. 148.)

HOW TO BUILD A HUMAN

It's extraordinarily tricky to build an animal like you – or a plant, mushroom or seaweed for that matter.

It all starts with a single cell, a fertilized egg cell. But we need a LOT more than one cell to build a body. Making more cells is the easy bit. So, just as Luca did four billion years ago, that one cell needs to get multiplying, fast.

Next, those multiplying cells need to stick together, like the bacteria did when they started creating a biofilm.

Then if this baby is going to have a head, a set of limbs, internal organs and all its other crucial bits and pieces, we need different groups of cells to start looking different and acting in different ways. They need to become specialized, through a process biologists call *differentiation*.

Differentiation happens gradually. At first, as the baby – called an *embryo* at this stage – develops, it produces general-purpose cells that all look pretty much the same. Slowly, the cells start to take on more specific features and ways of working as the organs take shape.

And, by the way, it's not the mother who's guiding her baby's growth and development. Yes, she's keeping it protected and providing essential supplies – food, water, oxygen – but it's instructions stored in the embryo's own genes that make this whole extraordinary process happen.

For this to work out well, the different cells must communicate with each other all the time. For example, if this part of the early embryo is going to make the baby's brain, those cells need to:

• 'Read' the right bits of the genetic instructions (and ignore the rest).

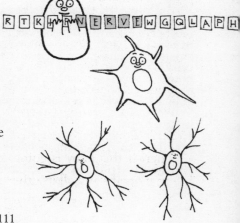

• Start turning into long, thin, chattering brain cells.

• Remember what they are doing, and stick to that task for the rest of their lives.

• And tell cells in other parts of the embryo . . .

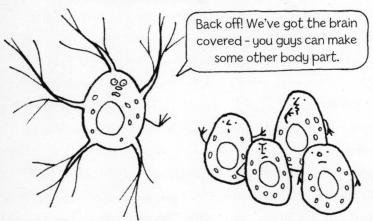

Back off! We've got the brain covered – you guys can make some other body part.

The development of a human baby is one of the most fantastically beautiful processes in the known universe, but it's so intricate and complicated that scientists don't know exactly how it happens. It's also amazingly reliable, for us and for all other animals. After all, most baby creatures are born with all the bits in the right places.

Building an entire walking, talking, breathing, burping multicellular animal from scratch couldn't have happened until eukaryote cells came on the scene. With their mitochondria power stations and other fancy organelles, they were gradually able to evolve larger and more complicated sets of genetic instructions. Then, around 700 million years ago, they built up the extra programs needed to construct a whole animal. And 698.8 million years later, the cells of some animals cobbled together all the genetic instructions they needed to build a fully functioning *Homo sapiens* ape like you, thinking brain and all.

Hello, we're your great-great-great-great ... 435 million generations later ... great-grandparents.

ALL FOR ONE, ONE FOR ALL

The individual bacteria that make up part of a biofilm can just up sticks and leave home whenever the going gets tough.

Hey, where are you going?

Luckily, your cells can't do that. All your cells are 100% committed to you.

We don't like your taste in shoes.

This is one of the biggest, most important differences between the bodies of animals and plants and the simpler collections of cells made by bacteria.

But how did true multicellularity evolve? Some organisms alive today give us a clue because their approach to multicellularity is halfway between the biofilm's 'take it or leave it' attitude and our fully committed 'we're all in this together' kind.

Slime moulds, for example, are microbes that mostly spend their lives as single, independent eukaryote cells, gobbling up bacteria in the soil. But if solitary slime mould cells run out of bacteria and start getting hungry, something very unexpected happens. All the cells in that patch of soil send out a signal, telling other nearby slime mould cells that they need to come and help. Then they all band together and form what looks like a 'slug'.

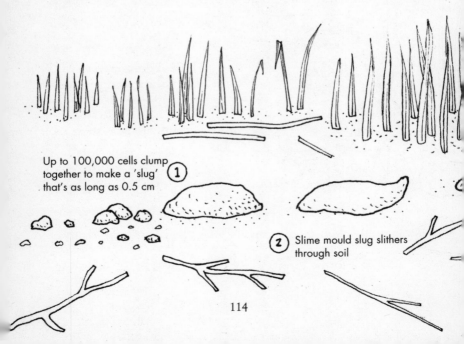

Up to 100,000 cells clump together to make a 'slug' that's as long as 0.5 cm **(1)**

(2) Slime mould slug slithers through soil

Slugs are definitely true animals, so this isn't a real slug. It just looks and acts quite like one – it can even wriggle through the soil.

When the slithering mass of slime mould cells finds a patch of earth that it likes, the cells reorganize themselves.

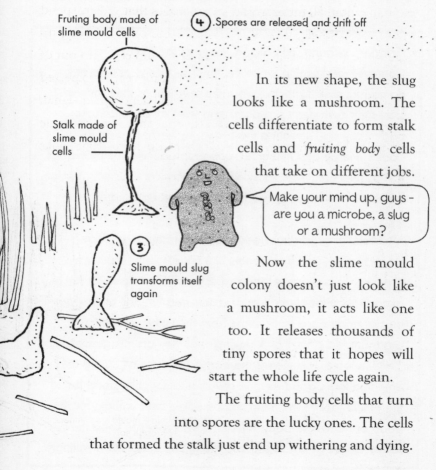

Fruting body made of slime mould cells

④ .Spores are released and drift off

Stalk made of slime mould cells

③
Slime mould slug transforms itself again

Make your mind up, guys – are you a microbe, a slug or a mushroom?

In its new shape, the slug looks like a mushroom. The cells differentiate to form stalk cells and *fruiting body* cells that take on different jobs.

Now the slime mould colony doesn't just look like a mushroom, it acts like one too. It releases thousands of tiny spores that it hopes will start the whole life cycle again.

The fruiting body cells that turn into spores are the lucky ones. The cells that formed the stalk just end up withering and dying.

Slime mould cells are a bit like the cells in your body: they can communicate with each other, work together and differentiate to do several different jobs. But there are important differences too. Cells in a slime mould colony are much more focused on their own success. If your cells were more like that, all order would soon break down.

Cancer: When Cells Stop Obeying the Rules

Cancers start forming when the inner workings of cells get damaged, making them ignore the instructions they receive from their own gene programs and from other cells in the body. They start cheating the system by hoovering up the body's energy and resources, often reproducing themselves as fast as they can. And, sadly, successful cancer cells can disrupt the rest of the body so much that they end up killing it.

Multicellular organisms need ways to protect their body from cheaters and freeloaders like cancer cells. That's why growing from a single fertilized egg cell is so essential for almost all animals, and lots of plants and fungi. If all the most crucial body parts have come from the same one cell, the organism has a way of 'knowing' that they are all, genetically, 100% related. This means the body's cells are all *clones* and anything that's good for one cell is automatically good for the others too. It's the main reason single cells will die for the good of the whole body. If that's what it takes to keep their fellow clones going strong into the future, they'll do it willingly.

Starting out with a single cell is great, but it's not enough to completely stamp out risks posed by rival cells or organisms. That's why your body devotes a lot of energy to building its immune system.

By the way, your immune system doesn't just fight off germs and diseases. Beating infections is only part of its job. One of its most important roles is telling the difference between 'self' and 'non-self'. By that, we quite often mean 'friend' and 'foe', except 'non-self' doesn't necessarily mean the same as 'foe'.

Just think of that piece of toast you ate for breakfast. It's definitely not part of you, so it must be 'non-self'. But it isn't your enemy either; it's your friend and you swallowed it for a good reason. You don't want your immune system to attack it.

On the other hand, your immune system doesn't always get these decisions right. Occasionally, it might decide that the toast (or the wheat inside it) is your 'foe', and trigger an immune, or allergic, reaction. And you'd be surprised what immune systems can learn to accept as a 'friend'.

The tentacles of the jellyfish-like Portuguese man-of-war contain deadly stinging cells that can kill large fish and people. Who would want one of them as a friend? Well, there's a certain kind of sea slug that does, in its own unique way. These sea slugs munch up those lethal tentacles, but instead of completely digesting them, they send the Portuguese man-of-war's stinging cells out to live in their own skin.

Somehow, the sea slug's immune system learns not to attack these dangerous foreign visitors, so the slug ends up with its own living layer of lethal defensive weapons.

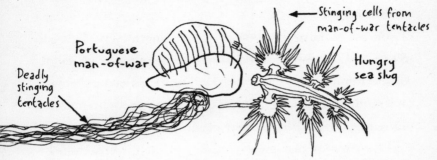

All sorts of creatures find stable ways of living and working alongside cells from completely unrelated organisms. Even that massive clump of cells that you think of as your body is, at the very most, only half human.

YOUR MICROBE MATES

Yes, YOU are only half human! For every human cell your body contains, there's at least one other entirely non-human cell too. These include a mixture of thousands of different species of bacteria, archaea and fungus cells. Together biologists call these cells your *microbiome*.

Most of the cells that make up your microbiome are extremely tiny, so together they only add up to a small fraction of your total body weight, but they're there all the time, in truly mind-boggling numbers.

Your microbiome doesn't see you as a person at all, it thinks of you as an entire landscape, just waiting to be colonized, mined, farmed and harvested for its natural riches. Bacteria cling to the cliff faces of your teeth and lurk inside the dimples on your tongue, sharing leftover bits of your meals. They hide out in huge swarms in the safe, warm and moist gaps between your toes and under your armpits. The rich, fertile soils of your intestines support the biggest, most diverse microbial communities of all – there could be a hundred different species of bacteria living in your gut right now.

Recently, biologists have even found communities of bacteria flourishing deep inside our lungs –

Teethcliff Heights
Tonsil Town
Tongue Hill
River Saliva
Gumdale
Lipswich

a part of the body they believed should be free of all intruders – even when we're in perfect good health.

Some of the microbes that live inside us cause infections

that can make us ill. Many more of them are as harmless as moss growing on a tree trunk. And lots more still are there because they do us good. In fact, we'd be pretty stuffed without our microbiomes. Here are just some of the many things they do to keep you going strong. They:

• Help digest your meals. Without them, most of what you eat would just pass straight through you and out the other end.

• Churn out various nutrients and vitamins that human cells can't make.

• Fend off germs that want to attack your body.

• Help your immune system learn the difference between 'friend' and 'foe'.

• Make substances that affect your brain, changing your mood or making you crave certain food.

Even though the trillions of individual cells that make up your microbiome come and go all the time, your microbiome is definitely part of you – and, luckily, the cells of our immune systems are quickly taught to treat it as 'self' from the moment we are born. If they tried to fight it off, they'd do you great harm.

So the immune system isn't just there to defend the body from intruders at all costs, it's also needed to welcome the right kinds of guest and make sure they feel at home.

Most animals, from the tiniest shrimps, to the largest whales and everything in between, have at least some communities of microbial cells living in them as vital parts of their multicellular bodies.

Hawaiian bobtail squid. Glowing bacteria help them hide from predators

Termites. Can digest solid wood thanks to bacteria that live in their guts

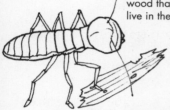

What we call a 'coral' is a mixture of animal, algae and various kinds of bacteria all living and working together

So it's not just the human cells in our multicellular bodies that are amazing. The very far from human ones, including the trillions of minuscule bacteria that keep us going day to day are amazing too. We need them as much as they need us.

A thank-you at last! Now you're starting to see why we microbes matter.

CHAPTER 9
Saved by the Cell?
USING CELLS TO KEEP PEOPLE AND THE PLANET HEALTHY

Think of a time when you fell and grazed your knee. It hurt, it bled . . . part of your skin was scraped right off.

But you probably didn't worry too much. Maybe you had an itchy scab for a bit but, chances are, your cells organized themselves to grow back and do a pretty good patch-up job. Within a couple of weeks you'd probably forgotten you'd ever hurt yourself.

Skin's impressive stuff. But fixing cuts and bruises is nothing compared to what flatworms can do.

- Chop one in two and both pieces will grow back to

> I want to be just like you when I grow up.

make two entire, perfectly formed flatworms.

• Chop one into 279* tiny pieces and each piece can grow back into a whole flatworm in just a few weeks.

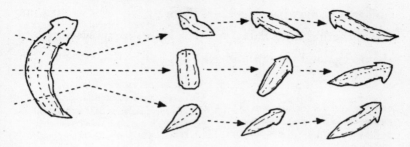

What if you'd had a much worse accident and cut a whole toe off? It'd be truly extraordinary if you could regrow a new toe. But the way flatworms heal themselves is far more impressive. It's the equivalent of your severed toe regenerating an entire new, flawless you!

*This is based on an actual experiment, from 1898, which showed that a tiny piece, equivalent to 1/279th of a flatworm, can *regenerate* a new worm.

Some biologists think flatworms never grow old and that they might be able to keep on regenerating themselves for ever (unless a hungry beetle gobbles them up whole). And it's not just slithering little flatworms that have superpowers to heal themselves and fend off old age:

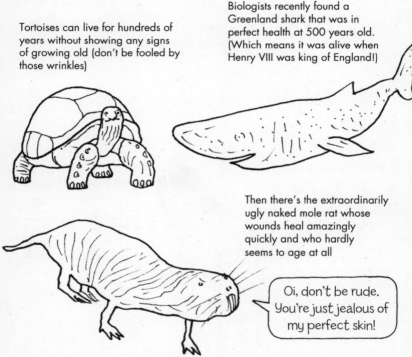

Biologists recently found a Greenland shark that was in perfect health at 500 years old. (Which means it was alive when Henry VIII was king of England!)

Tortoises can live for hundreds of years without showing any signs of growing old (don't be fooled by those wrinkles)

Then there's the extraordinarily ugly naked mole rat whose wounds heal amazingly quickly and who hardly seems to age at all

Oi, don't be rude. You're just jealous of my perfect skin!

Oops, sorry, mole rat, maybe you're right. If only we could understand how you do it. Maybe we could use your tricks to revitalize and repair our own bodies whenever we get ill or start to grow weaker with age?

SPROUTING FROM STEM CELLS

All multicellular bodies contain *stem cells* – cells that haven't differentiated (it's like they haven't made up their minds about what they want to do when they grow up).

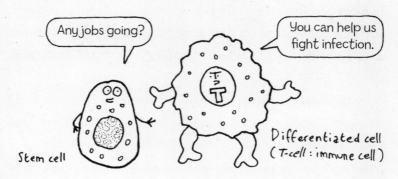

Stem cell

Differentiated cell
(*T-cell* : immune cell)

Stem cells give flatworms and, biologists think, naked mole rats, their powers of regeneration.

We know that all humans and most other animals start out as a single cell. That single fertilized egg cell is the ultimate stem cell. It has the potential to divide itself and create every kind of differentiated cell that's needed to make a whole body. It's the tiny stem that an entire creature grows from.

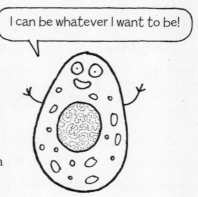

As we grow up, the cells in our body grow up too. Most of them differentiate. They stop being stem cells, stop dividing and settle into one particular job that they'll stick with for the rest of their lives. As they do this they flip some genes 'on' and lots of other genes 'off'. For example, a fully differentiated skin cell has to flip 'on' the gene programs needed to make skin, and flip 'off' the ones for making liver, brain, bone and everything else.

Something similar happens to the stem cells in our bodies. As we grow up, our bodies gradually come to contain fewer and fewer stem cells as more of them differentiate – which makes sense because we eventually stop growing. And it's only early embryos that contain completely undifferentiated stem cells. For the rest of our lives, the stem cells that remain are part-differentiated. Biologists call them 'tissue-specific' stem cells, because they can divide to make certain kinds of cell, but not every kind of cell.

For example:

• Skin stem cells are scattered through the deep layers of your skin. These are the ones that help heal grazed knees. They also make new cells to replace the dead cells that are constantly flaking off your body.

• The marrow at the centre of your bones contains blood stem cells that keep dividing to replace all the white and red blood cells that you lose each day.

• Stem cells in the walls of your intestines are constantly churning out new cells to maintain the lining of your gut.

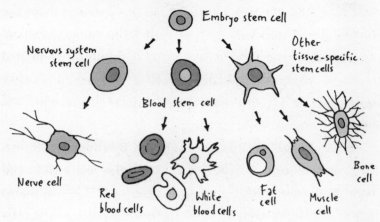

These tissue-specific stem cells are great – they keep our bodies going – but they're no match for the stem cells in a flatworm. Flatworms have far more stem cells than humans – they make up about one in every five cells in an adult worm – and each one of those stem cells has the power to make every cell in the worm's whole body.

Scientists used to think that the differentiation of our cells was a one-way journey. In other words, skin cells couldn't 'retrain' as liver cells and, after we're born, none of our cells could turn back into the kind of stem cells found in a newly fertilized embryo.

Then, in 2006, a Japanese scientist called Shinya Yamanaka did an experiment that shattered this whole idea. He took some fully differentiated skin cells from an adult mouse and transformed them into cells that looked and divided just like true stem cells. He claimed they could become any other kind of mouse cell and had the potential to regenerate a whole mouse!

Many scientists simply didn't believe Yamanaka's results – it was as if he'd wound back the clock to turn grown-up cells back into embryo cells.

But he wasn't making anything up. By flipping 'on' just four normal mouse genes, the skin cells really did turn back into stem cells. Yamanaka described the process as cell reprogramming and called the cells it produced *induced pluripotent stem cells,* or *iPS* cells for short.

Final proof that Yamanaka's claim was spot on came a couple of years later when biologists in China managed to use iPS cells to make mouse embryos, which grew up to become totally normal adult mice.

> Why would you guys care about what stupid little mouse cells can do?

> Watch it, small fry! We're way smarter than you.

Sorry, Luca, but it's true. Scientists and doctors have actually learned a massive amount by studying our little rodent friends. On the inside, their cells are incredibly similar to ours. If a revolutionary experiment works on mice cells, it very often works on human cells too.

Grow Your Own Organs

And that's what happened with cell reprogramming. A few months after their first breakthrough, Yamanaka's team sent human cells all the way back in time to an embryo-like state too. Just by taking a small and completely painless sample from anyone's skin or blood, it became possible to make completely undifferentiated human iPS stem cells.

The potential seemed enormous. Could doctors take these stem cells and use them to heal any damaged body part, from arteries to lungs, nerves, bladders, bones and beyond? And how about using them to grow whole new internal organs to use in transplants?

When an organ is transplanted from one person's body into someone else's, there's always a risk that the new body will see the transplanted organ as 'non-self' and reject it. But if the organ was grown from a patient's own cells, their immune system would be far more likely to see it as 'self' and hold off an attack.

Growing new organs sounds amazing but, unfortunately, it's much easier said than done.

Somehow, flatworm stem cells 'know' how to reconstruct an entire worm from scratch. A stem cell that lives in the tip of a worm's tail understands when it has to divide – and when it has to stop dividing – to produce just the right number of throat cells, mouth cells, eye cells and so on. And all those cells know how to end up in the right place at the right time. It's almost as if each stem cell contains a little map of the whole flatworm body.

Human iPS cells, on the other hand, seem to have lost their map (or perhaps they never had one). They can't automatically grow new organs, in a lab or inside a body. In fact, things could go very wrong indeed if doctors did start injecting iPS cells into us willy-nilly. Suppose the stem cells didn't know when to stop dividing? They could turn into aggressive tumours and cause life-threatening cancer.

Believe it or not, from first discovering a new technique to using it in a real-life situation can take up to 20 years. So scientists working on iPS cells are being extremely cautious. They've started by exploring health conditions where they think stem cell treatments are less likely to go wrong. One of those conditions is macular degeneration, an eye condition in which cells in the retina (the light-detecting layer at the back of the eye) die. Each year it causes millions of people to gradually lose their sight as they get older.

Here's how an iPS cell treatment would work:

1. Take a small piece of skin from a person with macular degeneration.

2. Grow the cells in the lab.

3. Turn 'on' Yamanaka's four genes. After a week or two some of them will turn into iPS cells.

4. Grow lots of iPS cells and then treat them with a mixture of different chemicals that differentiate them into retina cells.

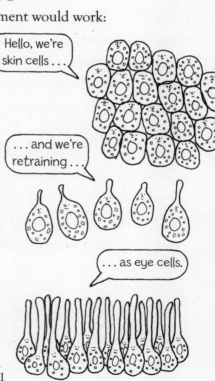

5. Inject these new retina cells into the patient's eyes so they replace those lost in macular degeneration.

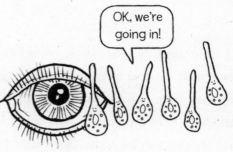

One of the neat things about using iPS stem cells in this way is that once they've differentiated into retina cells they can no longer divide, so they're very unlikely to cause cancer. So far only a handful of patients have had this treatment, but results are looking promising.

And it's not just stem cells that can help with treating diseases. Scientists are now coming up with all sorts of exciting new ways to use other kinds of human and non-human cells instead of chemical medicines.

Thanks to a ground-breaking new kind of science called synthetic biology, some blood cancers that were once untreatable can now be cured. Doctors take white blood cells from the patient's own blood and add new gene sequences to form what are called *CAR T-cells*. When CAR T-cells are injected back into the patient's blood, they home in on cancer cells like laser-guided missiles and destroy them!

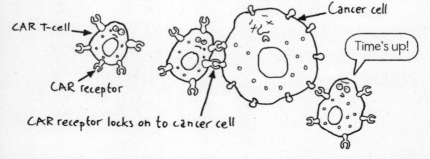

Synthetic biologists look at living cells in the same way engineers look at machines: as things to invent, tinker with and improve in order to get stuff done. Inspired by the success of CAR T-cells, they're inventing ways of using cells like tiny robots that can be released into our bodies and programmed to deliver treatments or repair damage precisely where and when it's needed.

Robo-cells reporting for duty!

These 'living medicines' are complicated and expensive treatments, but with a lot more research and a bit of luck that should change in the years to come. Those cancer-seeking CAR T-cells could be just the start of a full-blown medical revolution.

Super Cells to the Rescue

It'd be great if synthetic biology could help keep our bodies fit and healthy for longer, but it could do much more than that. It could help us repair some of the damage we've done to the whole world.

133

As we build bigger cities, farms and industrial plants, and as we criss-cross more of the planet with roads, runways and power lines, we're constantly destroying natural habitats – from hedgerows to entire rainforests – much faster than they can grow back. The pollution and plastic that escapes from our cars, planes, factories, fields, homes and rubbish tips is poisoning many other habitats. And, just as the cyanobacteria that caused the Great Oxygen Catastrophe did two billion years ago, our actions are changing the planet's atmosphere. Cyanobacteria turned the Earth into a giant snowball, but what we're doing is having the opposite effect.

Lots of our activities are pumping out greenhouse gases, especially carbon dioxide, methane and nitrous oxides, in massive amounts. When these gases build up in the atmosphere, they act like the glass in a greenhouse – and they're already heating the planet to danger levels. As the climate keeps getting hotter, life will get much tougher for many living things, including humans.

This is grim news, and we humans will have to mend our ways if we're going to protect natural habitats and ourselves. But it's not too late for us to prevent catastrophe and, believe it or not, cells might be able to help us tackle all these enormous challenges.

> Eh? But that's your problem, not ours!

True, we got ourselves into this mess. But if we can use other cells to put things right, we could make this planet a more hospitable place for all sorts of living things.

Here are a few of the big projects synthetic biologists are working on.

1. Cells Instead of Fossil Fuels

Scientists have already re-engineered cells from algae that can turn sunlight into diesel and other liquid fuels. They're 'carbon neutral' because when they're burned they only give off the carbon dioxide that they absorbed while they were alive.

And cells have been re-engineered to produce high-quality bioplastics, that are just as good as the ones we usually make from crude oil today.

In the future, cells like these could help us to give up burning fossil fuels (coal, crude oil and natural gas) altogether.

2. Cells to Help Feed the World

Right now the world has a lot of hungry mouths to feed. Most of us rely on intensive farming systems that hoover up huge amounts of energy, water and damaging chemical fertilizers, pesticides and weedkillers, as well as producing a lot of greenhouse gases.

If synthetic biologists can create food plants that grow much more efficiently . . .

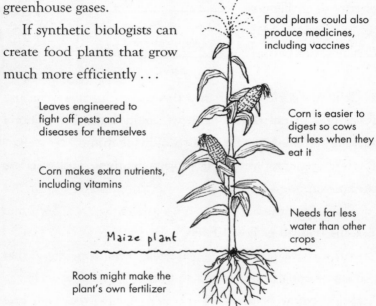

Food plants could also produce medicines, including vaccines

Leaves engineered to fight off pests and diseases for themselves

Corn is easier to digest so cows fart less when they eat it

Corn makes extra nutrients, including vitamins

Maize plant

Needs far less water than other crops

Roots might make the plant's own fertilizer

. . . fields could produce bumper crops, without needing to be sprayed with artificial chemicals.

We might even eat meat without killing a single animal. Scientists have already managed to take stem cells from a cow and used them to 'grow' edible burgers in a lab.

3. Cells Against Plastic

How cool would it be if we could get rid of and recycle our rubbish by feeding it to cells, rather than burying it, burning it, or letting it poison our rivers and seas? Garbage-gobbling cells that quickly chomp through plastics, fabrics and other kinds of hard-to-recycle waste could be coming our way soon. Synthetic biologists are rejigging powerful enzymes from bacteria that really can eat our waste.

4. Cells to Tackle the Climate Crisis

Right now, green plants, algae and seaweeds do a great job of sucking carbon dioxide out of the air as they photosynthesize. But we're generating emissions faster than they can keep up, so scientists are working on ways to encourage them to:

• Photosynthesize even more efficiently, to absorb and store even more carbon dioxide.

• And grow more easily in places where they might be starved of water or nutrients.

If all goes well, these cells could actually help to stop or eventually even begin to reverse global warming.

DO NO HARM

This all sounds very exciting, but we've got to look out for any new hazards that re-engineered cells might expose us to.

What if super-efficient
photosynthesizing plants
ended up doing too
well and started
spreading out of
control, damaging
other life forms?

What if they did their job then died in massive numbers? Their decaying bodies could spill all the greenhouse gases they'd absorbed back into the atmosphere. We'd be back where we started.

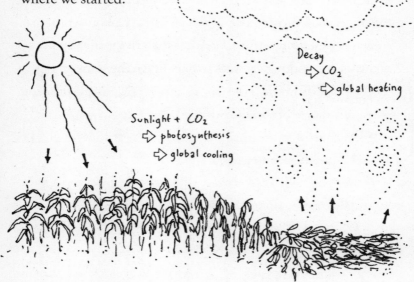

Decay
⇨ CO_2
⇨ global heating

Sunlight + CO_2
⇨ photosynthesis
⇨ global cooling

These sorts of risk have to be taken seriously, but they shouldn't stop scientists from trying to invent new kinds of cell. After all, doing nothing is extremely risky too. If we go on living as we are today, life on this planet could get very uncomfortable indeed.

The same goes for using synthetic biology, stem cells and other cell technologies on our own bodies. Before a new treatment can be put into regular use, scientists have to be sure it won't do more harm than good.

We also have to think ahead. For example, it's possible that scientists will discover ways to stop our cells ageing altogether. That could mean that you might go on living a healthy, active life for centuries to come, just like those sprightly centenarian tortoises and Greenland sharks.

But is that necessarily a good thing? Do we really want to go on patching up our cells and our bodies so we can live for ever?

Scientists find it hard to agree on these things; after all, they're mind-bending concepts. But it is important we talk about this stuff. Just because scientists **can** do something, doesn't mean they **should**.

And as we've already seen with cell reprogramming, what seems impossible today can become fairly straightforward tomorrow. Even so, we'll probably need several breakthroughs before eternal youth is an option. Scientists have learned all sorts of amazing things about how cells work, but they know they've really only scraped the surface. There's no way anyone could build even a simple living cell from scratch, and creatures like flatworms are still way ahead. Their cells can do stuff that we can still only dream of.

CHAPTER 10
Luca's Planet

You wouldn't believe what's going on inside your skull at this very moment. You've got billions of nerve cells in there. On their own, they're not so very different from any other kind of cell, but look what happens when they stretch out, wire together and start chatting among themselves. Those cells wake up! They have ideas! They read books! Not bad for a bunch of chemicals bumping around inside a membrane wrapper.

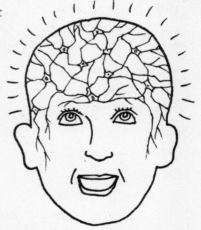

Thanks to our big brains, we humans have done pretty well for ourselves.

Remember Luca's plan for world domination? It's us who dominate the world now.

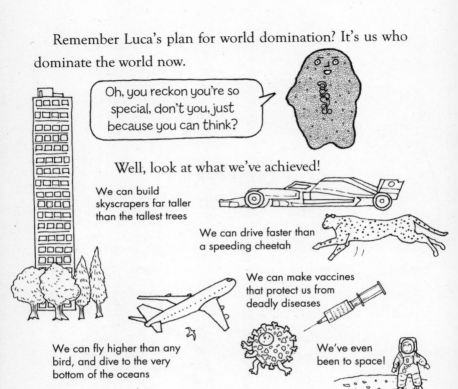

Oh, you reckon you're so special, don't you, just because you can think?

Well, look at what we've achieved!

We can build skyscrapers far taller than the tallest trees

We can drive faster than a speeding cheetah

We can make vaccines that protect us from deadly diseases

We can fly higher than any bird, and dive to the very bottom of the oceans

We've even been to space!

And, in the last hundred years alone, we've increased our population four times, from less than two billion to nearly eight billion people.

Yeah, whatever, but you can't compete with plants.

Well, it's true that plants really have flourished. If you had a big enough set of scales to weigh all the different living things on Earth, it would probably look as though plants are the most successful cells of all.

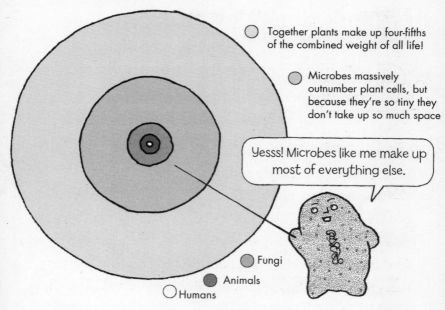

Together plants make up four-fifths of the combined weight of all life!

Microbes massively outnumber plant cells, but because they're so tiny they don't take up so much space

Yesss! Microbes like me make up most of everything else.

Fungi

Animals

Humans

The full circle represents the total weight of all living things. The shaded sections roughly show the estimated weights of each kind of living thing

All human beings combined add up to just one ten-thousandth of all living matter.

And you lot can't even fend for yourselves. All I needed was a bubbling vent.

Hmm, OK, you might have a point there, Luca.

All the food we eat is made by other living things, mainly plants, or animals that eat plants. We'd be stuffed without them; actually, we wouldn't be stuffed.
We'd be very hungry indeed.

> And what about your microbiomes?

Yup, if all you little microbe cells suddenly vanished, we'd get ill almost immediately and quite probably die.

Plant cells may not be able to farm cows or build planes, but they are much more independent than we are, because they're powered by sunlight. But even they can't grow without the help of other cells. Plant cells still need bacteria and fungi that create soils and capture and share crucial nutrients that plants can't make for themselves.

And remember the bacteria that turned into mitochondria and triggered an explosion of eukaryote life? Those bacteria might have given up their independence, but they took control of the cells of every animal, plant and fungus, whose bodies would immediately grind to a halt without mitochondria.

> You're finally starting to get it. We microbes are still in charge of this planet.

It's not a competition, Luca. We're all in it together. And actually, pretty much all living things, from amoebas to zebras, depend on other living things to some extent. They eat other cells, infect them, scavenge their waste, trade chemicals with them or find protection inside their bodies.

Yes, but none of those cells would be able to do anything if I hadn't divided in the first place!

OK, Luca, you're right. You did achieve something pretty special back in your day.

Humans haven't found a way to live for ever – yet. But Luca was born four billion years ago and, thanks to the art of self-reproduction, is still going strong! Part of Luca lives on in every one of us, and in every other cell that's alive today.

It's as if all the world's cells are parts of the same colossal creature. A creature that came alive when Luca first divided. A creature that has gone on developing and growing ever since. A creature that eventually wrapped the entire planet in a buzzing network of ambitious, evolving cells.

There is one thing that makes our human cells a bit special, though. Unlike Luca, or any other collections of cells as far as we know, we can ask big questions about how the world works. It's how we've been able to find out about Luca and cells in general, but that's just part of the story. There is so much more to discover – about how genes work, how life evolves, what brains are . . . But those are questions for other days, to be answered in other books.

We've come to the end of this book, but it's not the end of life's story. Thanks to Luca, cells are here to stay. We humans might go on thriving for millions of years to come. Or we might mess things up and wipe ourselves out completely. But life as a whole doesn't care. Cells will find a way to keep on going, regardless of what happens to us. We can only guess what wild new adventures they'll have in the wide-open future.

Now that's what I call immortality.

TIMELINE OF EARTH, CELLS AND ALL LIVING THINGS

Living creatures on this timeline are shown at the estimated time they first appeared on Earth.

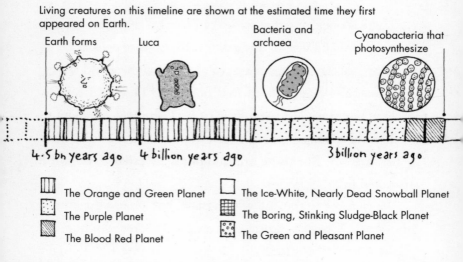

Earth forms

Luca

Bacteria and archaea

Cyanobacteria that photosynthesize

4.5 bn years ago   4 billion years ago   3 billion years ago

	The Orange and Green Planet		The Ice-White, Nearly Dead Snowball Planet
	The Purple Planet		The Boring, Stinking Sludge-Black Planet
	The Blood Red Planet		The Green and Pleasant Planet

TIMELINE OF KEY SCIENTISTS RESEARCHING CELLS

This timeline represents 2,500 years of scientific history. It shows all the scientists who appear in the book, but many more have built on their discoveries to expand our understanding of how cells work.

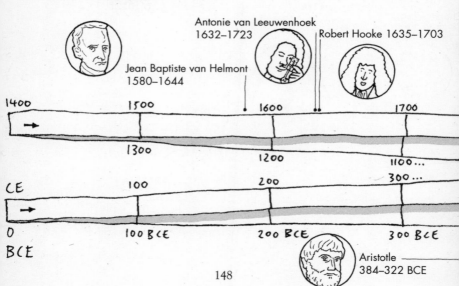

Antonie van Leeuwenhoek
1632–1723

Robert Hooke 1635–1703

Jean Baptiste van Helmont
1580–1644

1400   1500   1600   1700

1300   1200   1100...

CE   100   200   300...

0   100 BCE   200 BCE   300 BCE
BCE

Aristotle
384–322 BCE

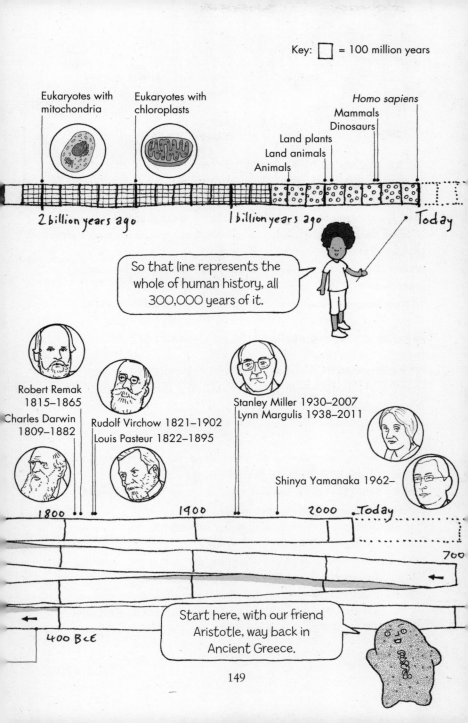

Key: ☐ = 100 million years

Eukaryotes with mitochondria

Eukaryotes with chloroplasts

Homo sapiens
Mammals
Dinosaurs
Land plants
Land animals
Animals

2 billion years ago

1 billion years ago

Today

So that line represents the whole of human history, all 300,000 years of it.

Robert Remak 1815–1865

Charles Darwin 1809–1882

Rudolf Virchow 1821–1902
Louis Pasteur 1822–1895

Stanley Miller 1930–2007
Lynn Margulis 1938–2011

Shinya Yamanaka 1962–

1800

1900

2000   Today

Today

700

400 BCE

Start here, with our friend Aristotle, way back in Ancient Greece.

149

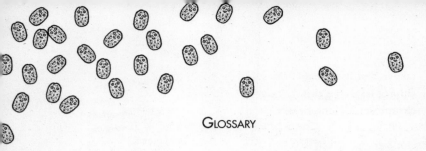

Words that are in italics have their own entries in this glossary.

~ approximately

algae a varied group of *organisms* that *photosynthesize*, but are not plants. Most live in water as single cells or as larger seaweeds and pond scums

alkaline the opposite of acidic. Alkaline substances can react with acids to neutralize them

amino acids small molecules; the 'building blocks' that link together to make *proteins*

archaea microscopic single-celled *organisms*; one of the three main kinds of living thing

atoms these extremely small particles bond together to build up all living and non-living things

ATP (adenosine triphosphate) a *molecule* that works like a battery, storing and transferring energy inside *cells*. ATP keeps the cells of all living things alive

bacteria tiny, single-celled *organisms*; one of the three main kinds of living thing

BCE before the common era (CE), which began in the first year of the calendar that is widely used around the world

biofilm a thin but strong layer of *microbes,* joined together by sticky substances made by the *cells* themselves

carbohydrate *molecules*, including sugars and starches, that provide and store energy for living things

CAR T-cells a type of *T-cell* that scientists have adapted so they find and kill specific cancer *cells* that are causing a patient's cancer

cell the smallest thing that can definitively be called 'alive'. Cells can live on their own as single cells, or together as parts of larger bodies

chlorophyll a chemical that allows plants, *algae* and *cyanobacteria* to take in and use energy from sunlight

chloroplasts *organelles* that can *photosynthesize*

chromosomes long *DNA molecules*, with *proteins* attached, that contain a *cell's genes*

clone an exact copy

cyanobacteria *bacteria* that can *photosynthesize*

cytoplasm a gel-like substance that fills the insides of *cells*

cytoskeleton a network of long, connected *protein* fibres inside a *cell*. The cytoskeleton gives a cell its shape, protects it, moves things around inside it and also allows some cells to move themselves around

differentiate/differentiation a *cell* differentiates when it changes from one kind of cell into another. Usually that means it becomes specialized to do a particular job, e.g. the cells in an *embryo* differentiate to make all the different organs of a baby

DNA (deoxyribonucleic acid) long, string-like *molecules* that carry information and form a *cell's genes*

embryo a living thing that is going through the earliest stages of its development

endoplasmic reticulum (ER) a network of tubes inside a cell where *proteins* and *lipids* are built and checked

endosymbiosis where one living thing (usually a *microbe*) lives inside the body, or the *cells*, of another living thing

enzyme a substance in a *cell* that can make, break, change or join together different kinds of *molecule*. All cells need lots of different enzymes to survive

eukaryote a living thing with *cells* that contain a *nucleus* (e.g. animals, plants and *fungi*)

fertilize when an egg from a female animal or plant joins together with sperm from a male animal, or pollen from a male plant, to create a new *embryo*

fruiting body the part of a *fungus* that produces *spores*

fungus/fungi mushrooms, yeasts, toadstools, mildews, moulds and infections like 'athlete's foot'. They can be single *cells* or collections of lots of cells and feed on decaying material or other living things

gene/genetic each gene contains a specific instruction for how to build a particular part of a *cell* or body. Genes are made from *DNA* and are passed down from one generation of a living thing to the next

Golgi apparatus an *organelle* that finishes, sorts and packs newly made *proteins*, *lipids* and *carbohydrates*, before sending them to the part of a *cell* or body where they are needed

hydrothermal vent a crack, or 'fissure', in the seabed through which hot water and gases escape, mixing with seawater

Homo sapiens the *species* you belong to. Modern humans

immune system a network of *cells* that work together to protect a body from infection. It is able to recognize things that are likely to cause harm

infrastructure buildings and facilities, such as roads, sewers and power stations, that enable a human city to function

insatiable can't be satisfied

iPS cells (induced pluripotent stem cells) *stem cells* that are made by undoing the *cell differentiation* process, making them work like the kind of general-purpose cells found in *embryos*. They can be used to make all the other kinds of cell in a body

lichen a slow-growing living thing that is part *fungus* and part *algae* or *cyanobacteria*. It often grows on trees, rocks and walls

lipids oily substances that make up *cell membranes*, store energy and carry signals inside cells

lysosome an *organelle* that helps break down and recycle different materials within the *cell*

membrane a thin layer of *lipids* that surrounds a *cell* and creates different compartments and *organelles* inside it

microbe/micro-organism a living thing that is too small to be seen without a microscope

microbiome a collection of different *microbes* that live in a particular place, such as the trillions of *microbial cells* that live on and in a human body

mitochondria the *organelles* that create most of a cell's energy-carrying *ATP molecules*

mitosis when one *cell* divides to make two cells, which both contain an identical set of *genes*

molecule two or more *atoms* joined together

multicellular/multicellularity living things with bodies made from lots of *cells* that are all working together

nerve *cells* or collections of cells that carry electrical signals and impulses around the brain and body

nucleic acid *DNA* or *RNA*. Chemical substances that form *genes* and do other essential jobs inside all living *cells*

nucleus a *eukaryote cell's* main control centre, which contains the *genes*

offspring new *cells* or living things, made when parents *reproduce*. Including children

organelle a part of a *cell* with a particular function; it usually has its own *membrane* wrapper

organism a living thing

parasite a life form that lives on or inside another living thing, getting food or other benefits from its host without giving anything back

peroxisome an *organelle* that gets rid of toxic substances within the *cell* and produces some *lipid molecules*

photosynthesis/photosynthesize the process through which plant and *algae cells* use energy from sunlight to convert water and carbon dioxide into energy-containing sugar *molecules*

pore a tiny hole or opening, e.g. in the skin or cell membrane, that allows substances, such as liquids or gases, to pass through

proteasomes structures in *cells* that break down unwanted *proteins*

protein a large *molecule* that is essential for all living things. Proteins have many functions in *cells*, including building structures, controlling chemical reactions and sending and receiving messages

protist a *eukaryote organism* that isn't an animal, plant or *fungus*, e.g. *algae* are protists

receptor a structure in a *cell membrane* that responds to a stimulus (such as light, touch or the presence of a particular *molecule*) and triggers a reaction inside the cell

regenerate/regeneration when animals and plants grow new parts to replace those lost or damaged

reproduce to produce new copies of a living *cell* by cell division; or to make a new generation of living things

ribosome a structure found in all living *cells* that turns the instructions contained in *genes* into *molecules* of *protein* that can then work for the cells

RNA (ribonucleic acid) a chemical with a similar structure to *DNA*. One of its main jobs is delivering messages from *DNA genes* to the rest of the *cell*

self-reproduction when a *cell* or *organism* makes a copy of itself

semen the fluid that carries sperm in male humans and other animals, which can *fertilize* a female egg

species a particular kind of *organism*. Members of a species have similar characteristics and share relatives

spontaneous generation the theory that lifeless substances, such as mud and water, can suddenly create new life forms

spore a small *cell* that can grow into an entire new organism. *Fungi* and some kinds of plant, *protist*, *algae* and *bacteria* use spores as a way to self-reproduce

stem cell a general-purpose *cell* that can divide itself to make new cells, which then *differentiate* to do specific jobs. Particularly important when bodies grow and heal

synthetic biologist a scientist who works on creating living *cells*, or parts of cells, that do not naturally exist. For example, by changing *bacterial chromosomes*, synthetic biologists make cells that produce non-polluting engine fuels for cars and jet planes

T-cell a kind of white blood *cell* that forms part of the *immune system*. T-cells launch very precise attacks on infections and sometimes on cancers

ultraviolet (UV) radiation invisible waves of light that can damage *cells*. UV radiation from the sun may have been 100 times more intense when Luca was born than they are today

virus a minuscule living particle that can only *reproduce* itself inside the *cells* of a different living thing. Some can cause diseases

INDEX

ACKNOWLEDGEMENTS

Just as it takes a lot of cells to build a body, it takes a lot of people to build a book like this. Our immense thanks to editor extraordinaire Helen Greathead, who steered this book's development from start to finish. We're massively grateful to dynamic designer Alison Gadsby, who gave the growing book much-needed form and structure. Huge thanks also to managing editor Anthony Hinton, for his clear and constructive input throughout. Thanks to Julia Bruce and Jennie Roman for their astute editorial efforts, to indexer Helen Peters and to the wider DFB team, including Bron, Fraser, Phil, Rosie, Meggie, Jasmine and Rachel, for their crucial work behind the scenes. This new and unique approach to non-fiction was dreamed up by David Fickling, and then shaped by Michael Holyoke and Liz Cross. Special thanks to Dr Michael Way, of the Francis Crick Institute, for checking our facts and letting us tap his deep expertise in cell biology.

BM: This book was made amid the Covid-19 lockdowns of late 2020 and early 2021. I am intensely grateful to Cal, not only for her keen edits and encouragement throughout, but also for shouldering more than her fair share of homeschool duties to make sure this text could take shape.

Ben Martynoga is a biologist and science writer. After a decade in the lab exploring the insides of brain cells, he swapped his white coat for a pen. Since then he has written about everything from the latest tech innovations to rewilding, running, stress, creativity, microbes and the history of science. He loves talking about science – and why it matters – with children and adults alike at science festivals, in classrooms or anywhere else. His writing appears in the *Guardian*, *New Statesman*, the *i*, the *Financial Times* and beyond. He lives, works, wanders and wonders (often all at once) in the Lake District.

Moose Allain is an artist, illustrator and prolific tweeter who lives and works in South West England. He runs workshops and has published a book and an online guide encouraging children to draw, write and find inspiration when faced with a blank sheet of paper. Always on the lookout for interesting projects, his work has encompassed co-producing the video for the band Elbow's 'Lost Worker Bee' single and designing murals for a beauty salon in Mexico City – he's even been tempted to try his hand at stand-up comedy. His cartoons regularly feature in the UK's *Private Eye* magazine.

In 2020, Ben wrote and Moose illustrated *The Virus*. They are currently working on more books in the *Explodapedia* series.

EXPL⬡DAPEDIA

The Cell is just one piece of a larger world of knowledge. There is plenty more to discover, and *Explodapedia* will be your guide!

Where will your curiosity take you next . . . ?

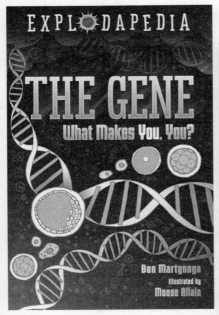